MATHS

OFFICIAL WORKBOOK

AGES 5–6

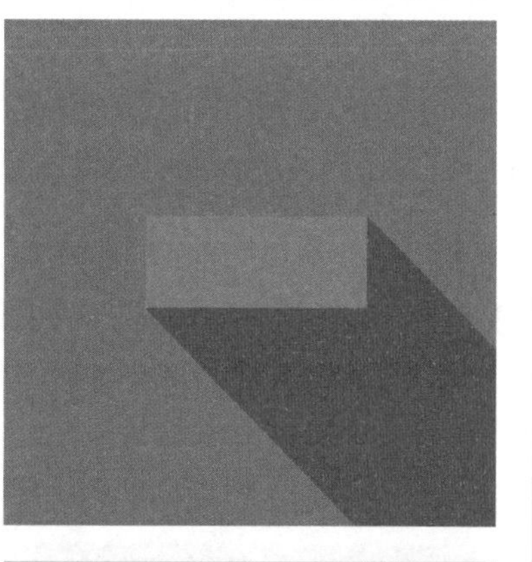

DAN LIPSCOMBE
AND BRAD THOMPSON

INTRODUCTION

HOW TO USE THIS BOOK

Welcome to an exciting educational experience! Your child will go on a series of adventures through the amazing world of Minecraft, improving their maths skills along the way. Matched to the National Curriculum for maths for ages 5–6 (Year 1), this workbook takes your child into fascinating landscapes where our heroes Jacob and Cali embark on building projects and daring treasure hunts...all while keeping those pesky mobs at bay!

As each adventure unfolds, your child will complete topic-based questions worth a certain number of emeralds. These can then be 'traded in' on the final page. The more challenging questions are marked with this icon to stretch your child's learning. Answers are included at the back of the book.

Note: While using this book, your child is likely to need some adult support, such as in reading explanations to them and giving any further help as necessary.

MEET OUR HEROES

Jacob loves making big things and small things – and everything in between! This busy lifestyle, constructing buildings and making tools, means he often works up an appetite. He really enjoys a piece of cake. His favourite colour is green...so finding emeralds on his adventures is just wonderful!

Cali adores exploring caves for precious ore. She rarely leaves home without her pickaxe. She is always wandering off when she spies an open cave and the shine of iron ore. Her favourite colour is gold...because of gold ore, of course! Cali also loves spending time with animals.

First published in 2021 by Collins
An imprint of HarperCollins*Publishers*
1 London Bridge Street, London, SE1 9GF

HarperCollins*Publishers*
1st Floor, Watermarque Building, Ringsend Road, Dublin 4, Ireland

Publisher: Fiona McGlade
Authors: Dan Lipscombe and Brad Thompson
Project management: Richard Toms
Design: Ian Wrigley and Sarah Duxbury
Special thanks to Alex Wiltshire, Sherin Kwan and Marie-Louise Bengtsson at Mojang and the team at Farshore

Production: Karen Nulty

ISBN 978-0-00-846274-1

British Library Cataloguing in Publication Data.

A CIP record of this book is available from the British Library.

1 2 3 4 5 6 7 8 9 10

Printed in the United Kingdom

MIX
Paper from responsible source
FSC C007454

This book is produced from independently certified FSC™ paper to ensure responsible forest management.

For more information visit: www.harpercollins.co.uk/green

CONTENTS

NUMBER AND PLACE VALUE

THE PLAINS: A GREAT BASE

The plains are large places to explore. With lots of flat grass, it's a great place to build a house. Chickens can be heard clucking; sheep, pigs and cows crowd under oak and birch trees which grow everywhere. Sometimes bees can be seen moving from flowers to their hive to make yummy honey.

LOTS TO FIND

There aren't many hills in the plains, but you'll find rivers filled with salmon swimming around. Along the river, sugar cane grows high. Everything in the plains is helpful. There are materials everywhere.

CREEPY NIGHTS

The plains can be dangerous at night. When it gets dark, all kinds of mobs come out to cause trouble. Zombies shuffle slowly, spiders climb nearby trees and skeletons fire arrows from far away. Creepers might be the scariest as they can explode when they get too close.

GETTING GOING

Jacob has spawned into the plains. He has nothing in his inventory, and he needs a place to live. Looking around, Jacob spots another adventurer. It's Cali! They decide to work together to build, craft and harvest. First, Jacob needs to find a good spot for his house...

NUMBERS AND COUNTING

Jacob starts to explore the plains. He finds a great spot to build a wooden house. Before he can start, he will need a crafting table.

1

Jacob collects some wood to make planks. He will make a crafting table from the planks. The planks are shown in the picture.

How many planks does Jacob use?

Jacob wants to plant some flowers in the grass around his house. Flowers can be used to make dyes. Dyes can be used to change the colour of different things.

2

Draw a line to join each box with the correct picture.

12 tulips	16 poppies	20 dandelions

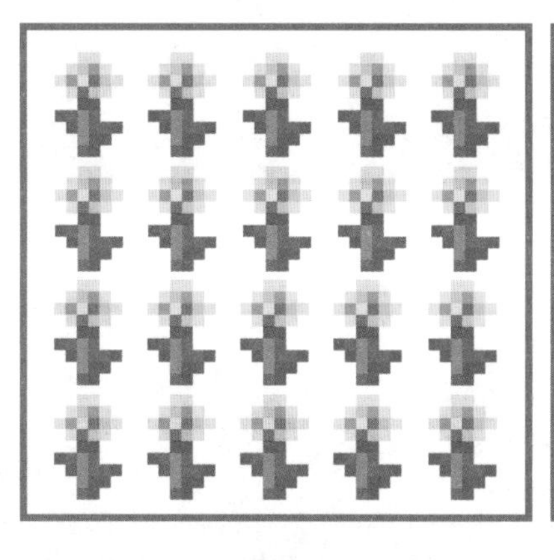
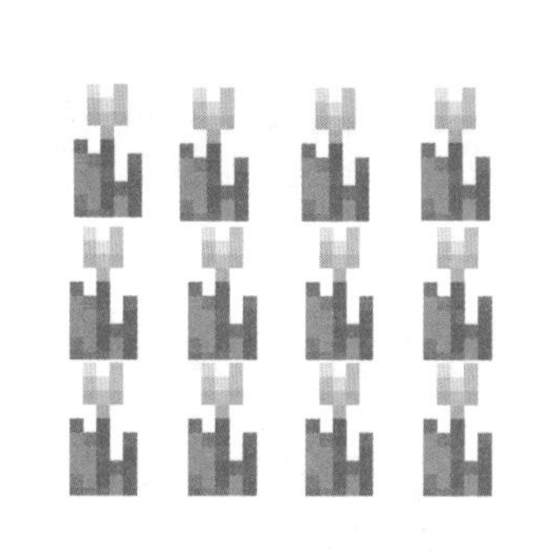
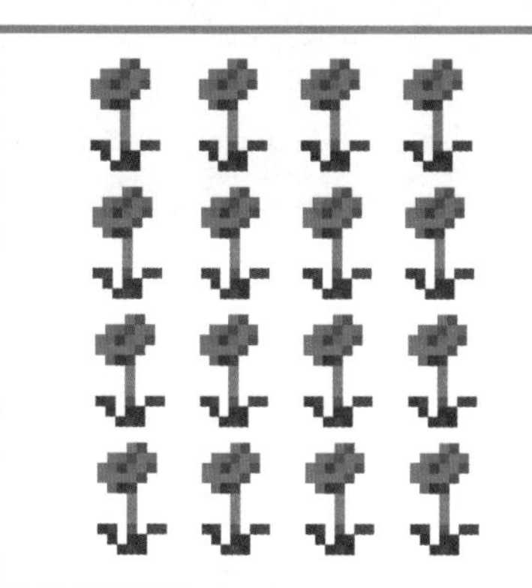

COLOUR IN HOW MANY EMERALDS YOU EARNED

COUNTING FORWARDS AND BACKWARDS

Jacob starts to build a wooden house by placing the walls. At each corner of the house, Jacob sets an oak log. Then he places a layer of oak planks. The blocks are numbered in order.

Which five numbers are missing on the layout of blocks?

Write the missing numbers in these boxes:

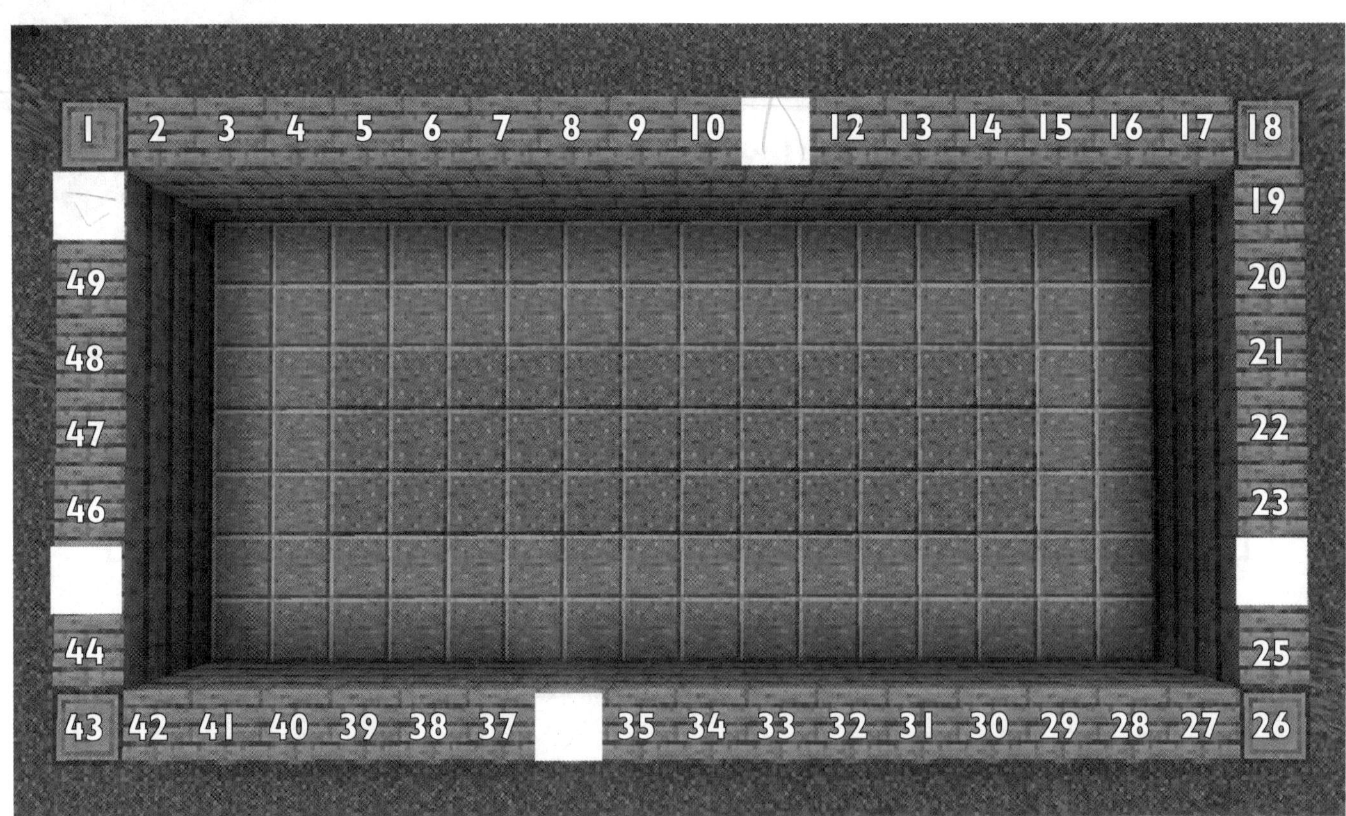

Jacob has finished the walls of his house. He wants a cobblestone roof to stop dangerous spiders climbing in. With his pickaxe, Jacob mines a patch of stone to collect materials.

2

Jacob is at block 24 and counts forwards the given blocks.

Write the block he lands on.

a) Counting forwards 2 blocks from block 24 = ☐

b) Counting forwards 7 blocks from block 24 = ☐

c) Counting forwards 9 blocks from block 24 = ☐

3

Jacob is at block 45 and counts backwards the given blocks.

Write the block he lands on.

a) Counting backwards 3 blocks from block 45 = ☐

b) Counting backwards 6 blocks from block 45 = ☐

c) Counting backwards 10 blocks from block 45 = ☐

COLOUR IN HOW MANY EMERALDS YOU EARNED

COUNTING IN STEPS OF 2, 5, AND 10

Jacob is going to build a stone wall all the way around the wooden house. He builds the wall so that he can keep an area for a farm. He plants seeds ready for harvest: the potatoes in groups of two, carrots in groups of five, and wheat in groups of ten.

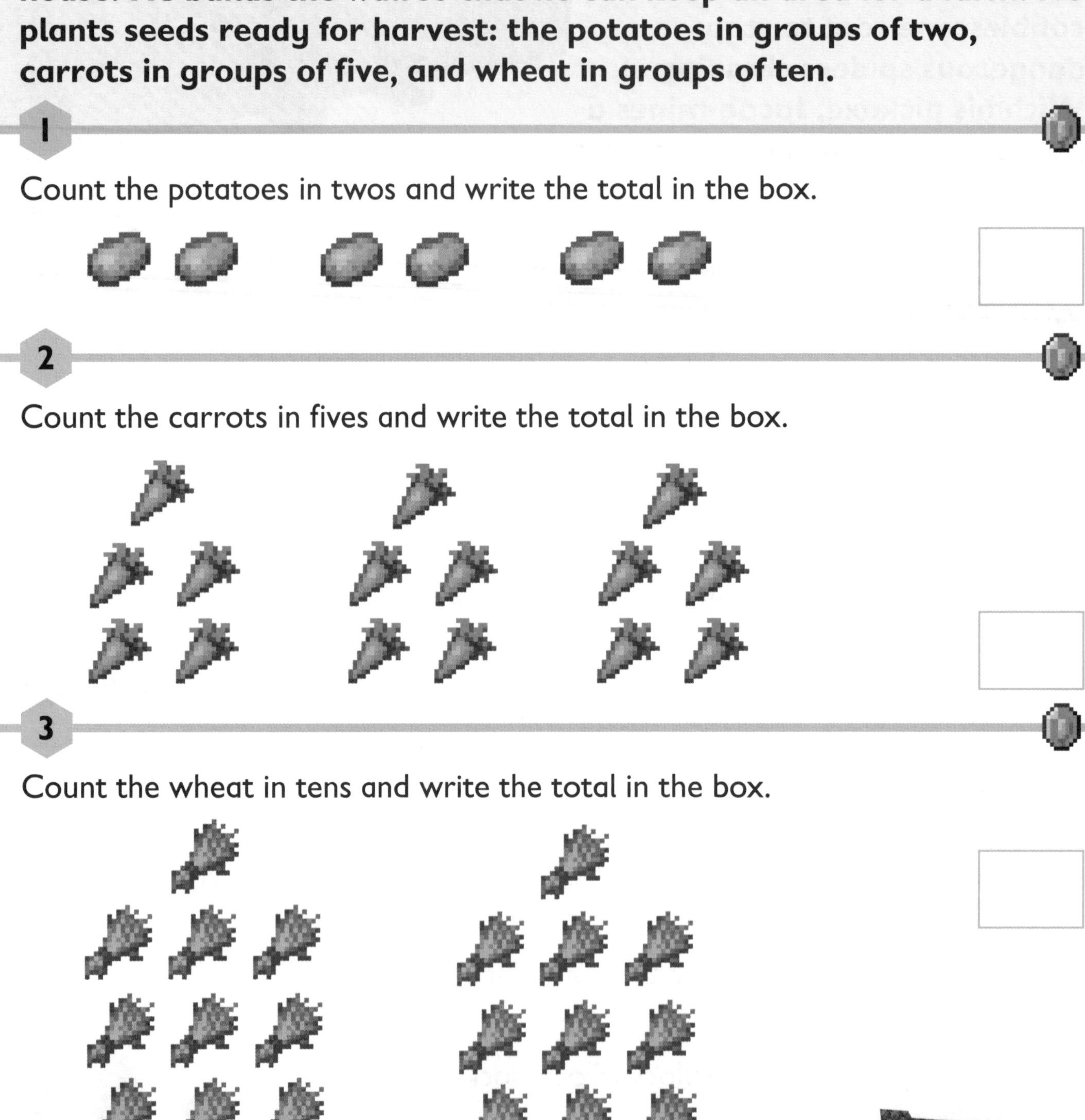

1

Count the potatoes in twos and write the total in the box.

2

Count the carrots in fives and write the total in the box.

3

Count the wheat in tens and write the total in the box.

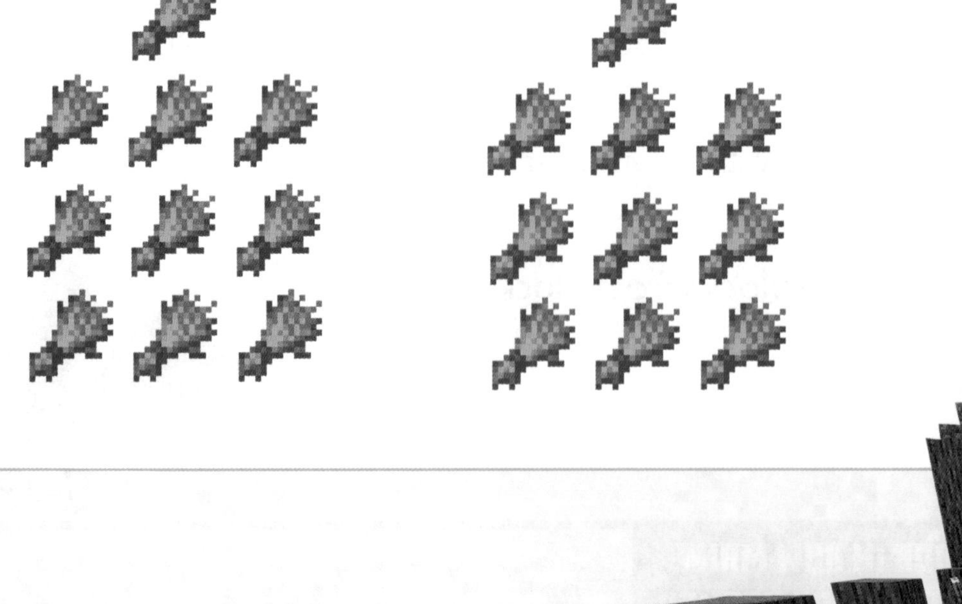

Jacob does some exploring and finds a village. Here he can trade some of the food he has grown in exchange for emeralds.

 4 

Each item of food can be traded for this number of emeralds:

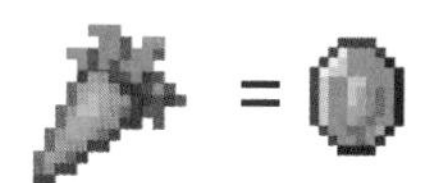 

The boxes show how many of each item of food Jacob will trade. Draw lines to join each box to the villager farmer who has the correct number of emeralds to trade for each amount of food.

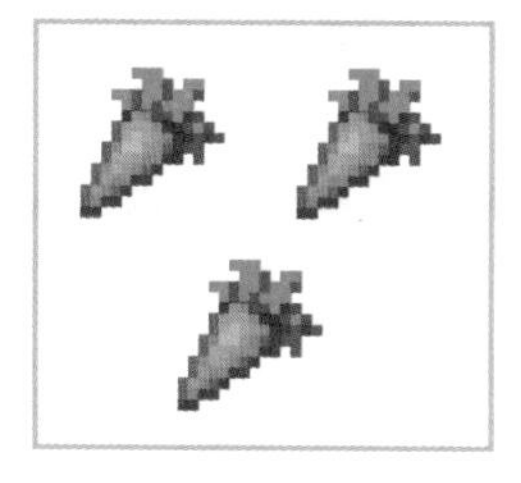 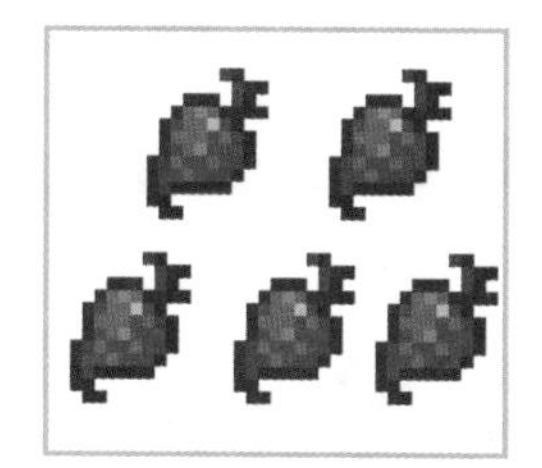 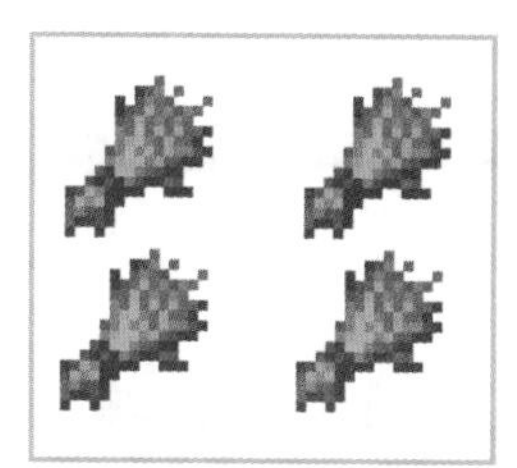

12

25

3

5

 Now Jacob has some emeralds to trade with, he buys 30 gold ingots from Cali.

= 1 emerald

Circle the correct number of emeralds needed to buy 30 gold ingots.

COLOUR IN HOW MANY EMERALDS YOU EARNED

COUNTING ONE MORE AND ONE LESS

Jacob returns home to find Cali has gathered lots of animals for the farm. Jacob decides to feed them. He needs help to look at his inventory and see what they can eat.

1

To feed all the animals, Jacob needs one more of each item.

For each item below, add one more and then write the total. There is space to draw one more if you want to.

a)  

b)  

c) 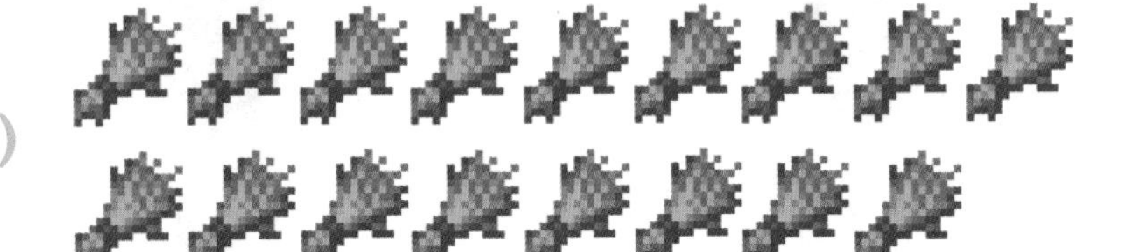 

d)  

e)  

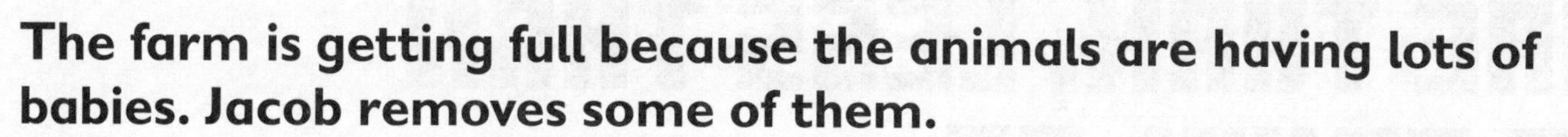

The farm is getting full because the animals are having lots of babies. Jacob removes some of them.

2

Jacob takes away one of each animal. For each animal below, find one less. Cross out one animal to help you. Write the answer in the box.

a)  

b)  

c)  

d) 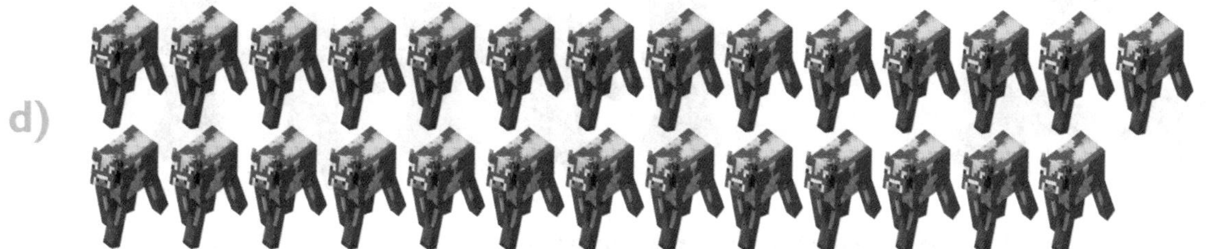 

e) 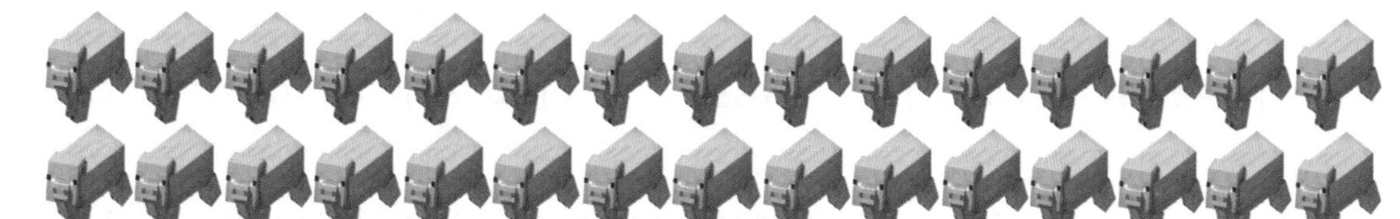 

Jacob is using bone meal to fertilise his crops. Bone meal makes plants and trees grow quickly.

3

 Jacob has **one more** bone meal than cobblestone and **one less** bone meal than coal.

Cobblestone 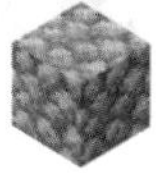

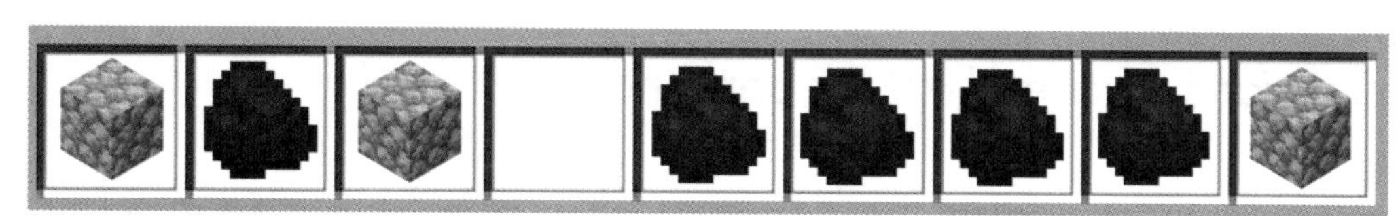

How much bone meal does he have? ☐

COLOUR IN HOW MANY EMERALDS YOU EARNED

MORE THAN, LESS THAN AND EQUAL TO

Jacob leaves home at night. Whilst he is out, he can see mobs of enemies everywhere. It's a busy night for hostile mobs!

1

Jacob can see two groups of mobs.

Circle the correct word to complete the sentence.

The group of spiders is **more** **less** than the group of zombies.

2

Jacob looks to the side and can see another two groups of mobs.

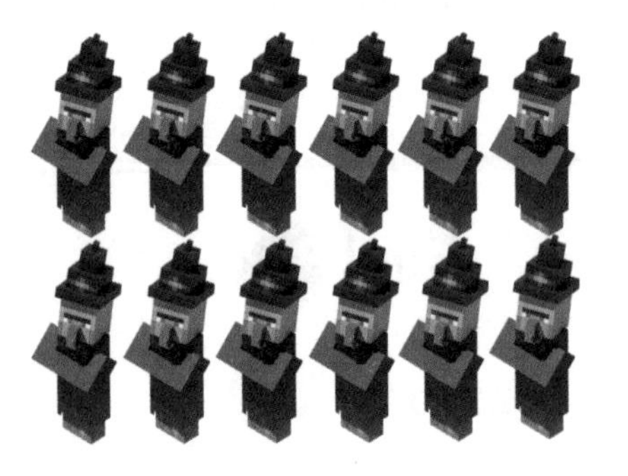

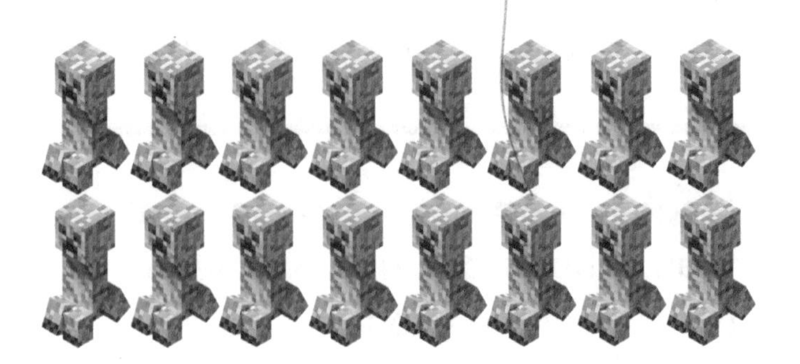

Circle the correct word to complete the sentence.

The group of creepers is **more** **less** than the group of witches.

Jacob is chopping down more trees for wood. As he harvests two oak trees, they start dropping apples.

3

Circle the tree that has dropped more apples than the other.

Jacob returns home and wants to shear his sheep for their wool. He has green sheep, red sheep and blue sheep. He shears them in the morning and in the evening.

4

The left side of each row shows the number of wool blocks sheared from each colour of sheep in the morning. The right side shows the number of wool blocks sheared from each colour of sheep in the evening. Compare the amounts that Jacob obtained in the morning and in the evening.

Write **more than**, **less than** or **equals** in the space in each row.

a)  .... 

b)  .... 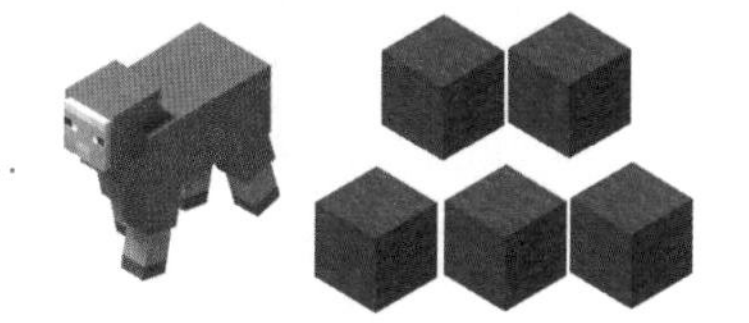

c)  .... 

COLOUR IN HOW MANY EMERALDS YOU EARNED

NUMBER REPRESENTATION

To obtain more resources, Jacob mines for iron. He explores a cave close to home. As Jacob digs, he leaves columns of stone. There are columns of ten stone and blocks of one iron ore.

1

What number of blocks is shown by each picture? Draw lines to join the pictures to the correct numbers.

10 | 19 | 13

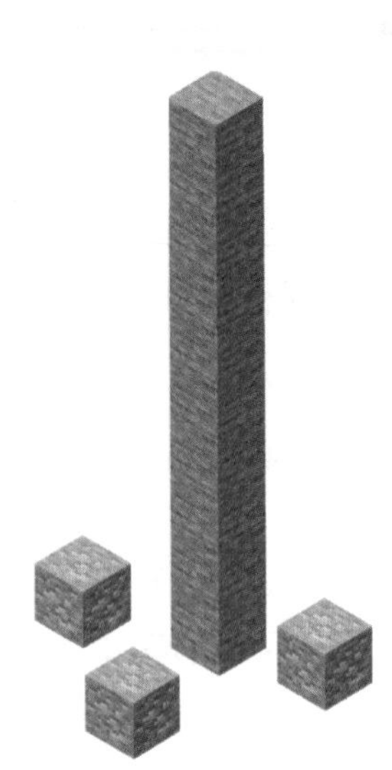

2

Write the numbers shown by the pictures.

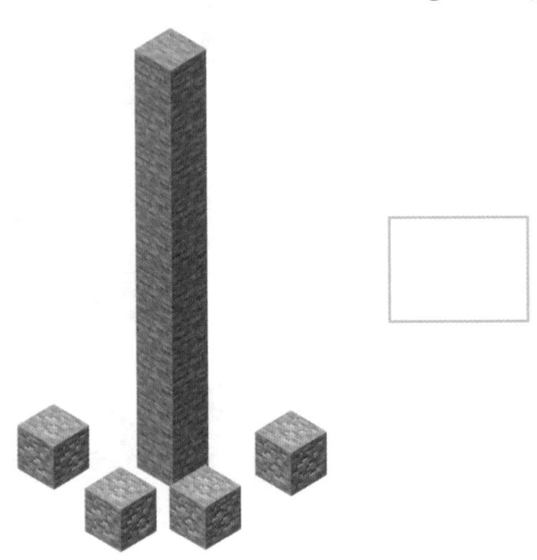

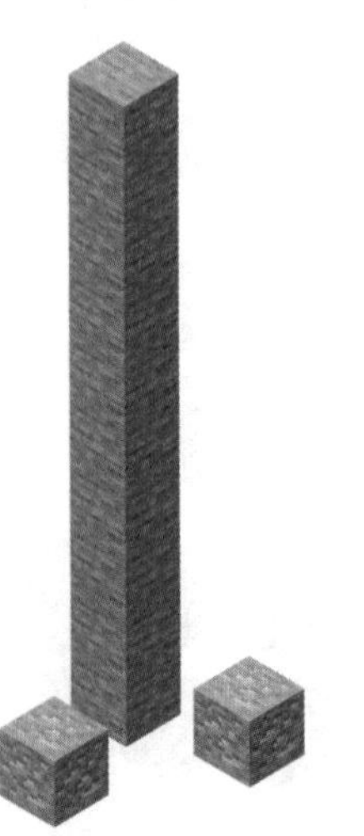

COLOUR IN HOW MANY EMERALDS YOU EARNED

ADVENTURE ROUND-UP

HOME SWEET HOME

Jacob has made a lovely home. Having explored the plains, he found lots of materials. Using these, Jacob built a small farm full of veggies and an area for Cali's animals. Now the house is a real base. It has two bedrooms, a small kitchen and lots of space for new items.

A HAPPY FARM

The animals seem happy. Every time they're fed, they have cute little babies. The food chest is filling up ready for eating. The farm needs more light to stop mobs from spawning and to make sure the animals are safe.

MORE TO DO!

There's still more to build and new tools to craft. Jacob and Cali would like different wood to build with. They also need a faster way to cook food as they get very hungry when exploring. Most of all, they need weapons and armour to protect themselves.

Jacob and Cali make a checklist:

- Need swords and armour
- More food
- Stock up on wood
- Find coal for torches and the furnaces

ADDITION AND SUBTRACTION

FRUITS OF THE FOREST

The Overworld is home to many forests. Different types of trees crowd next to each other. Mushrooms grow in the shadows under the trees and are very tasty in stew. Among the trees are shallow lakes filled with fish and patches of clay. There's plenty of wood and food.

TREES AND BEES

Occasionally the trees are spaced out and flowers bloom everywhere. These pretty areas are hard to find. Rabbits dash about and bees hover, collecting pollen. Forests can be very beautiful places to explore but are full of danger at night-time. It's best to be at home before the sun sets.

WALK HOME WITH A WOLF

Cows, pigs and chickens are common in forests, and wolves can sometimes also be seen. These wolves are quite friendly unless attacked. By feeding them bones, there's a chance to tame one and take it home.

HIGH HOPES

Cali enters a birch forest with only a stone sword, some food and an empty inventory. She hopes to bring back lots of helpful items. She wants to find extra food, but coal and iron are also important.

DOUBLING AND HALVING

Cali is in the forest looking for some mushrooms for a stew. She makes sure to check near the ground under the tall trees.

1

Cali finds four brown mushrooms.

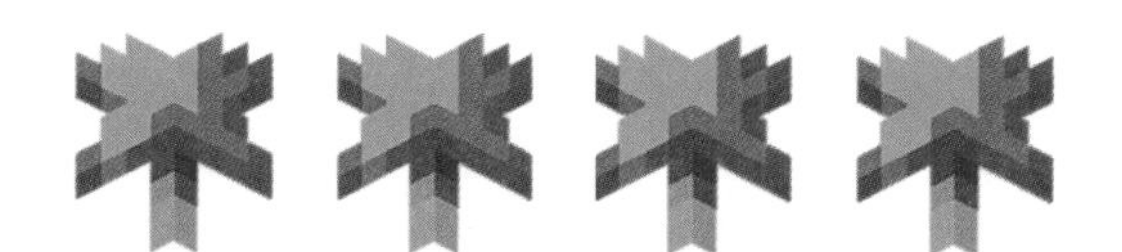

She needs the same number of red mushrooms to cook enough stew.

Show the red mushrooms by drawing them below the brown ones.

2

Now complete these number sentences.

a) Double 4 = ☐   b) 4 + 4 = ☐

Now Cali has mushrooms, she needs wood to craft some bowls. Cali has chopped down some birch trees and has 12 logs, plenty for planks. She decides to craft with half of the logs.

3

How many logs will Cali use? Cross out half of the logs.

4

Now complete these number sentences.

a) Half of 12 = ☐   b) 12 – 6 = ☐

COLOUR IN HOW MANY EMERALDS YOU EARNED

SOLVING ADDITION AND SUBTRACTION PROBLEMS

Cali explores deeper into the forest. She spots lots of rabbits and some bees. She has some carrots and tries to feed the bunnies.

Cali finds 4 rabbits. She finds another 5 rabbits.

Draw 5 more rabbits and write the total in the box.

Cali would like to craft some dye. Magenta is her favourite colour. She hopes to dye some wool for decoration. To craft magenta dye, she needs lilac flowers, which grow in the forest.

Cali has 12 lilacs in her inventory. She adds 8 more.

How many does she have in her inventory now?

12 + 8 = ☐

Cali stops to look through her inventory. Her food count is getting a bit low.

3 

Cali had 19 cooked porkchops when she started exploring. After walking, chopping and digging, she has 9 cooked porkchops left.

How many has she eaten?

19 – 9 = ☐

Cali manages to collect some apples. Each apple restores 2 drumsticks on the hunger bar.

4 

 After eating 4 apples, Cali's hunger bar is full.

How many full drumsticks must she have had in her hunger bar before she ate the 4 apples?

Colour this hunger bar to help you work it out and write your answer in the box.

☐

COLOUR IN HOW MANY EMERALDS YOU EARNED

USING TWO-DIGIT NUMBERS

Cali worries that mobs will be out soon. Luckily she found some iron ore while digging and can craft some armour. Using wood and cobblestone, she makes a crafting table and a furnace to work on armour.

Cali has 18 iron ingots. She crafts a chestplate and uses 8 of them.

How many iron ingots are left?

Cross out 8 iron ingots and write the answer in the box.

It's starting to get dark. Cali is approached by a group of 4 skeletons. She defeats them. Then she finds another group of skeletons and defeats them too.

2

Cali has defeated 8 skeletons so far. She then defeats 4 more skeletons.

How many skeletons has she defeated altogether? Draw 4 more skeletons and write the total number in the box.

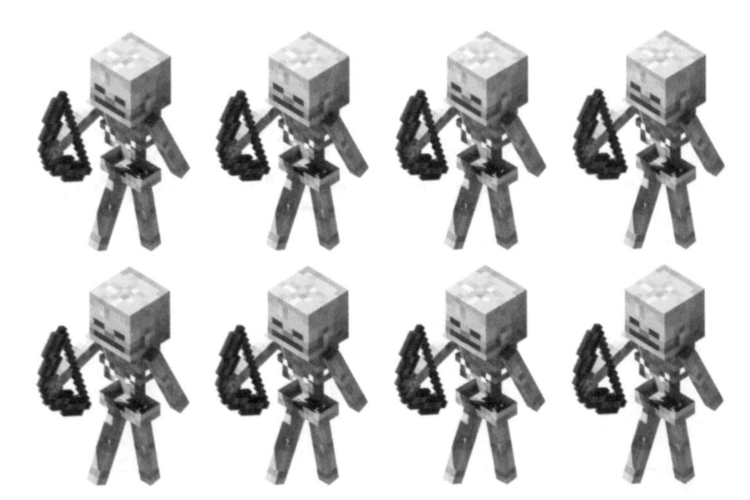

Cali decides it's time to get out of the forest and walk home. On her way she sees 8 zombies following her. In the distance she sees 8 more zombies.

3

What is the total number of zombies that Cali has now seen? Tick (✓) the correct answer.

8 ☐ 16 ☐ 20 ☐

As Cali wanders home, she realises that the house needs more light around it to stop mobs from spawning.

4

Cali has found 20 coal for torches.

Draw a line to join each question with the correct answer.

Cali uses up 5 lumps of coal. How many coal does she have left?	8 lumps
Cali uses up 12 lumps of coal. How many coal does she have left?	5 lumps
Cali uses up 15 lumps of coal. How many coal does she have left?	15 lumps

COLOUR IN HOW MANY EMERALDS YOU EARNED

NUMBER BONDS

Cali arrives home before the zombies get too close. She begins to craft torches and places them on blocks in the stone walls around the house. The walls are in rows of 10.

1

Look at the rows.

How many blocks with torches are used in each row of 10?

a)

8 + ☐ = 10

b)

6 + ☐ = 10

Now Cali wants to add torches to the sides of the house. Mobs spawn where there is no light. She has to stay safe.

2

Cali wants to use 20 torches altogether. She only has 11 left in her inventory.

How many more torches does Cali need?

20 = 11 + ☐

COLOUR IN HOW MANY EMERALDS YOU EARNED

ADVENTURE ROUND-UP

GOOD GATHERINGS

Cali has survived her trip to the forest. Discovering and exploring during the day was easy. She gathered plenty of wood and found iron ore and coal in a small cave among the trees. There were plenty of mushrooms to make stew. She saw lots of wildlife, too.

A BIT OF BOTHER

Cali ran into trouble a few times. She hadn't packed enough food for such a trip and had to hunt rabbits. She also stayed out longer than expected and had to prepare to fight mobs. To do this, she made iron armour.

PLAN AND PREPARE

Now she is home and ready for bed. Cali used her coal to make extra torches to keep the house safe. The rest will be used in the furnace to cook food. She learned that when exploring, she must be prepared. She talks to Jacob about what they must do next, and together they make a plan:

- Gather iron for full armour
- Create an iron golem for the house
- Granite for decoration

MULTIPLICATION, DIVISION AND FRACTIONS

LET'S GO CAVING

Caves are dark and spooky places to explore. Anything can be waiting around the corner! But caves are also full of treasure. Coal and iron ore are quite common underground. These can be used for important crafting recipes, like weapons and armour. The best materials are found very deep underground: diamonds!

MINING MISSION

Jacob has set out from home with a full set of iron armour and a sword. His inventory has plenty of food and tools; he's ready to go mining.

DIAMONDS AND DANGER

Diamonds are one of the hardest materials to find. Sometimes they are found near pools of lava. You never want to fall in the lava! Mining in these areas is very dangerous.

CAVE MONSTERS

In the darkness bats flap around, but they're no trouble. It's the mobs that cause a nuisance – zombies, spiders, skeletons, creepers… even slimes. Slimes are nasty and hard to fight. They break into separate slimes when attacked. They love large dark areas, just like these caves.

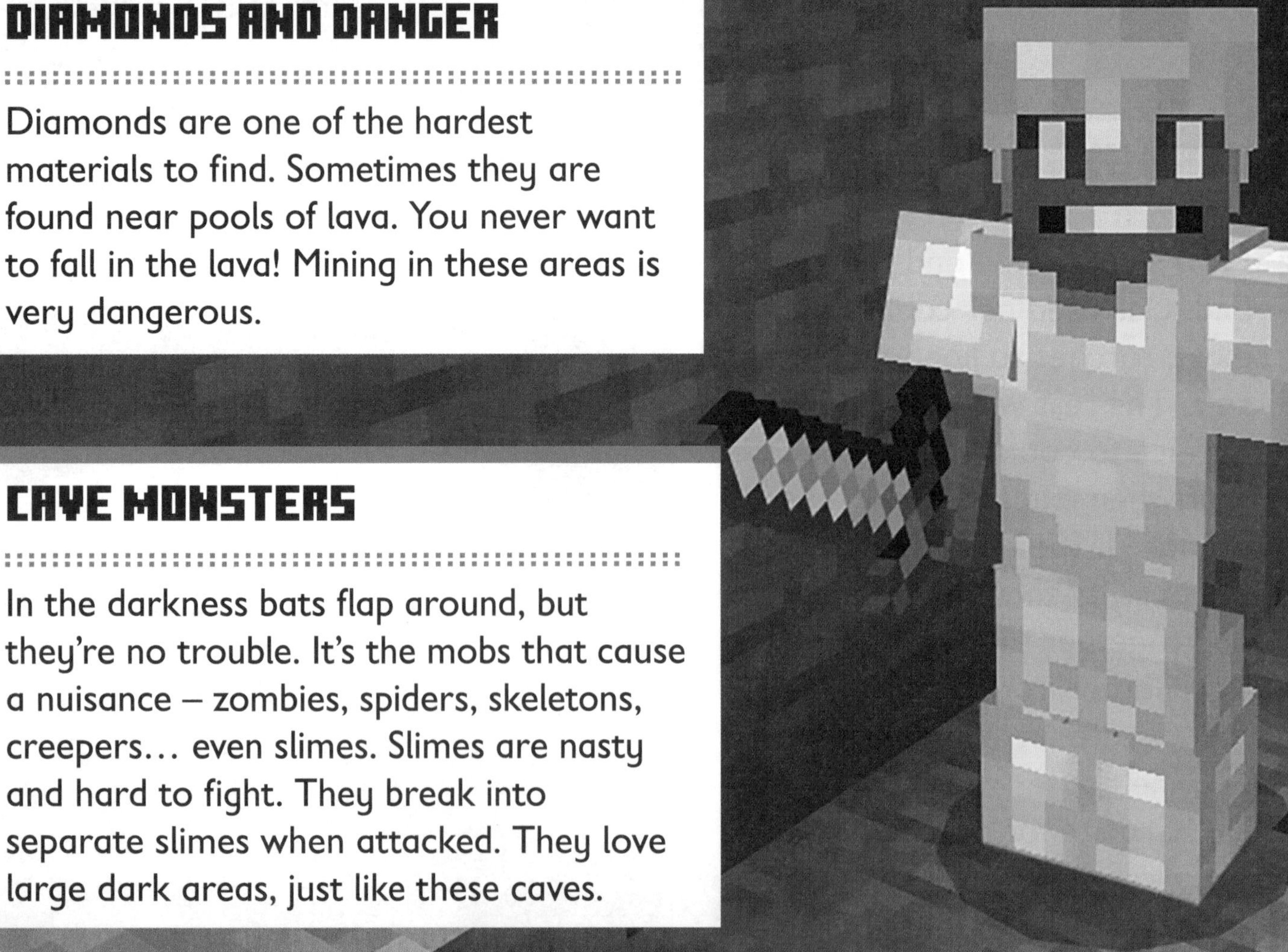

MULTIPLICATION

Jacob moves through the caves and finds a small area with plenty of ore. He places down a torch to help him see while mining. He can see some iron ore and gold ore close by. Jacob starts digging.

1

Look at the stone wall.

How many blocks of iron ore can Jacob mine altogether?

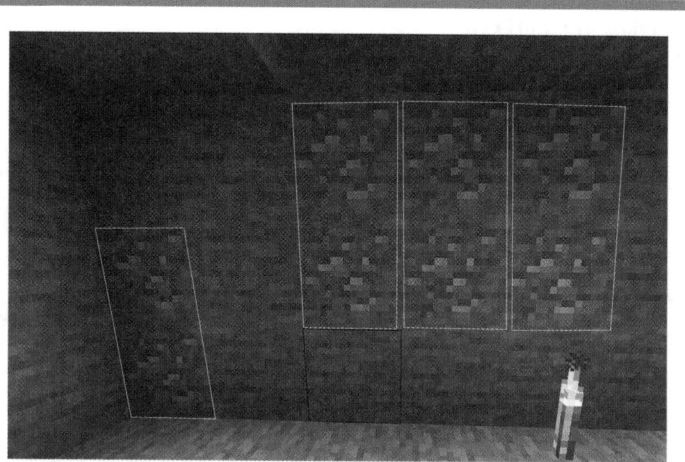

$4 \times 2 =$ ☐

2

Now look at this stone wall.

How many blocks of gold ore can Jacob mine altogether?

$2 \times 3 =$ ☐

3

Here is another stone wall.

How many blocks of coal ore can Jacob mine altogether?

$2 \times 5 =$ ☐

DIVISION

As he walks further into the cave, Jacob hears a noise behind him. He turns and spots some spiders crawling out of a corridor full of cobwebs.

1

There are 10 cobwebs in total.

Draw a circle around each group of 2 cobwebs.

2

Inside the cobwebs, Jacob finds a spider spawner. As he clears the webs, more spiders come out. There are 12 spiders in total.

Tick (✓) the box for the picture that shows 12 spiders shared between 3 different cave chambers.

3

Turning a corner, there are more webs! The spiders have spun 12 cobwebs across 4 chambers.

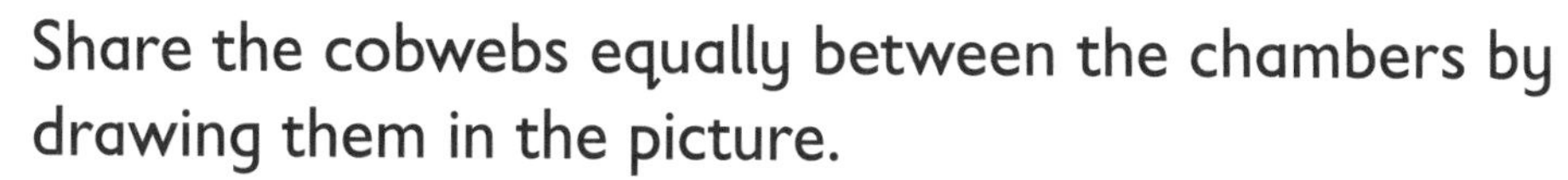

Share the cobwebs equally between the chambers by drawing them in the picture.

With the spawner broken and the spiders defeated, Jacob stops to look through his inventory. He needs more torches as he's been using a lot to guide his way. He will craft 5 bundles.

4

Jacob has 20 coal. He can't use them all for torches. He splits them between the 5 inventory slots.

How many coal will there be in each slot?

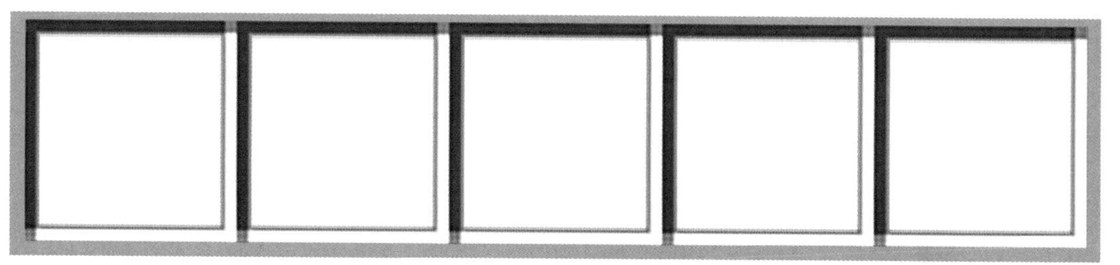

COLOUR IN HOW MANY EMERALDS YOU EARNED

2, 5 AND 10 TIMES TABLES

Jacob has been doing a lot of fighting. His sword is almost broken, so he decides to craft some more swords.

1

Jacob wants to craft swords out of iron. For each sword, he needs 2 iron ingots.

How many iron ingots does he need to make 3 swords? Draw the iron ingots to help you work it out.

3 × 2 = ☐

Jacob is very lucky. He has discovered an abandoned mineshaft. There are lots of minecart rails. They are placed in sets of five.

2

Jacob sees 6 sets of rails. How many rails in total does he see?

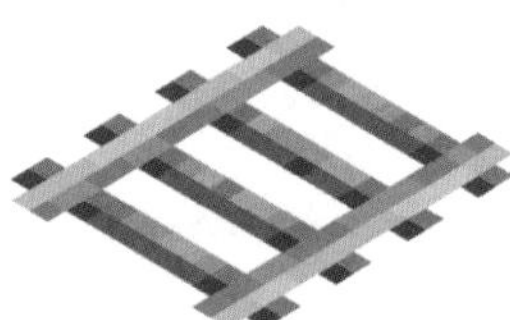

6 × 5 = ☐

The mineshaft is dark. Jacob has 10 coal. Each piece of coal can produce 4 torches.

3

How many torches can Jacob craft from 10 coal?

4 × 10 = ☐

Jacob remembers his list and mines granite blocks to make pillars back at the house. To make a granite pillar, you need 2 granite blocks.

2 granite blocks  =  1 granite pillar

How many granite pillars can Jacob make with:

a) 4 granite blocks? b) 8 granite blocks? c) 10 granite blocks?

Jacob finds a number of chests in the mineshaft.

5

Each chest contains 10 items. How many items are found in these numbers of chests?

a) 1 chest  ☐ items

b) 5 chests  ☐ items

c) 2 chests  ☐ items

COLOUR IN HOW MANY EMERALDS YOU EARNED

SOLVING MULTIPLICATION AND DIVISION PROBLEMS

Jacob is feeling brave. He spots a group of creepers and decides to fight them. Creepers drop gunpowder when destroyed and Jacob would like some to craft TNT.

1

Each creeper drops 2 gunpowder:

=

How many creepers will Jacob need to defeat to pick up 8 gunpowder?

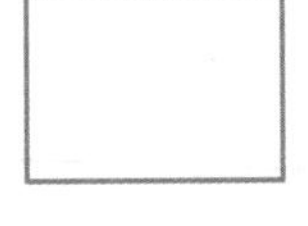

Jacob decides to set up a small base inside the cave, ready for future exploring. He places 5 furnaces to cook 20 porkchops. He shares the meat evenly across the furnaces.

2

How many porkchops are in each furnace?

Colour in the box that shows the correct answer.

2 porkchops

8 porkchops

4 porkchops

6 porkchops

Jacob starts to think about heading home. He starts to follow the torches out and runs into a slime. Slimes take a lot of hits to defeat because they split apart. To defeat a slime, it takes 20 damage. A wooden sword does 5 damage with each hit.

3

Tick (✓) the sentence that shows how many times Jacob needs to hit the slime.

5 damage to slime with each hit

20 hits × 5 damage = 20 damage ☐

10 hits × 5 damage = 20 damage ☐

4 hits × 5 damage = 20 damage ☐

There are more mobs! Jacob has to deal with some skeletons on the way out of the cave. Each skeleton drops 2 bones. When Jacob has defeated the skeletons, he collects all the bones.

4

Jacob collects a total of 18 bones. How many skeletons did he defeat? Colour in the box that shows the correct answer.

11 skeletons

9 skeletons

7 skeletons

5 skeletons

COLOUR IN HOW MANY EMERALDS YOU EARNED

HALVES AND QUARTERS AS FRACTIONS

It looks like the mobs have gone. Jacob had to work hard to defeat them.

This circle represents Jacob's cake. He has eaten the portion shaded purple:

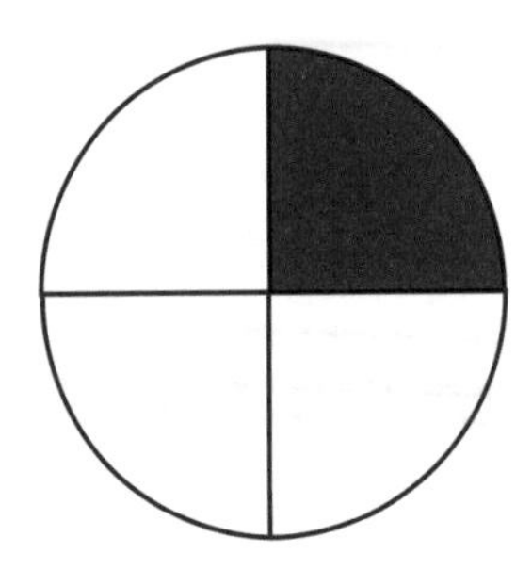

What fraction of the whole cake has Jacob eaten? Tick (✓) the correct answer.

One quarter 

One half 

Three quarters 

As Jacob wanders through the winding corridors, he realises his tummy is rumbling. It's no wonder, his hunger bar has gone down!

The picture shows how many of the 10 drumsticks in Jacob's hunger bar are filled. What fraction of a whole hunger bar does Jacob have left to fill?

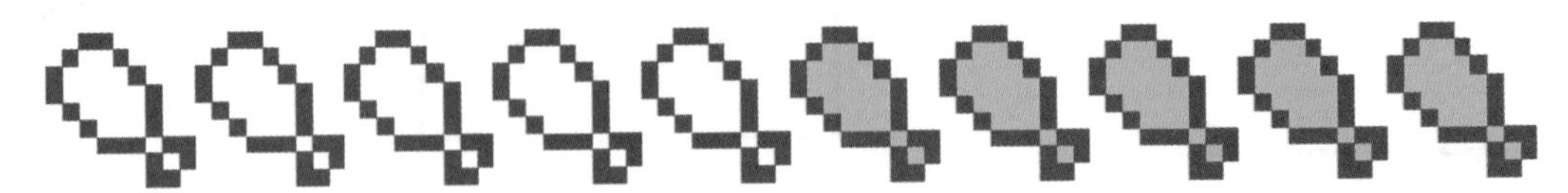

Write the fraction in the box. 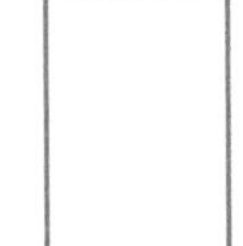

Lots of bats can be found in the caves. They don't drop anything when defeated, so Jacob just enjoys watching them flying around.

3

Jacob sees a group of 4 bats. One of the bats flies away, leaving 3 bats behind.

What fraction of the group of bats has flown away? Tick (✓) the correct answer.

One quarter ☐ One half ☐ Three quarters ☐

Jacob can see some iron ore in the side of a cavern. He must have missed it as he entered. It's quite high up, so he uses some dirt blocks from his inventory to build upwards.

4

The iron ore is 20 blocks from the ground.

Choose from the options in the box to answer each question below.

Halfway	Three quarters	One quarter

a) Jacob builds 5 blocks up. How close is he to the iron ore?

....

b) Jacob builds 10 blocks up. How close is he to the iron ore?

....

c) Jacob builds 15 blocks up. How close is he to the iron ore?

....

COLOUR IN HOW MANY EMERALDS YOU EARNED

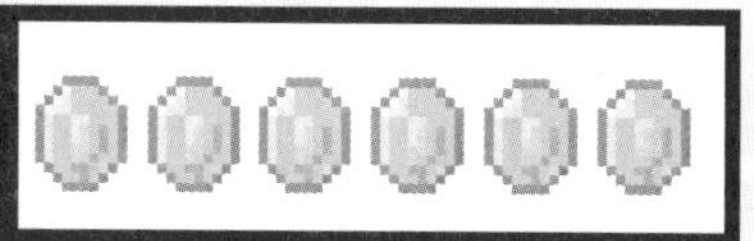

FRACTIONS OF NUMBERS

Jacob is finally out of the caves. He begins the short walk home, pleased with how many materials he found. He hopes he has enough iron to craft a golem. Jacob needs 4 blocks of iron and a pumpkin. He spots some pumpkins in the distance.

Jacob can see 8 pumpkins.

Circle half of the pumpkins and complete the number sentence below.

$\frac{1}{2}$ of 8 = ☐

To make the iron golem, Jacob needs to use shears to craft the pumpkin into a jack o'lantern. Then he decides to make some more jack o'lanterns, with torches inside, for the house.

Jacob has 8 pumpkins in his inventory.

Circle one quarter of the pumpkins for Jacob to craft into jack o'lanterns and complete the number sentence.

Inventory

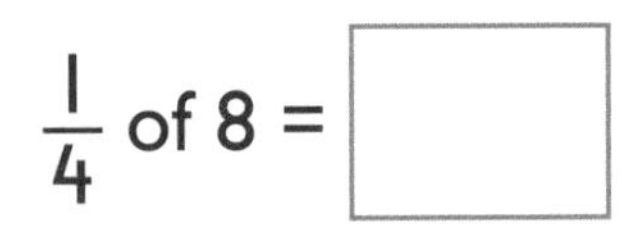

$\frac{1}{4}$ of 8 = ☐

COLOUR IN HOW MANY EMERALDS YOU EARNED

ADVENTURE ROUND-UP

TIME TO RECHARGE

Jacob arrives home tired. His adventure into the nearby cave system was exciting, but scary at times. He found lots of materials for crafting. Before he empties his inventory into chests, he stops for some dinner. Cali cooked up lots of lovely baked potatoes while he was gone. With a few of these, his hunger is gone and he spends some time dividing out his materials and items.

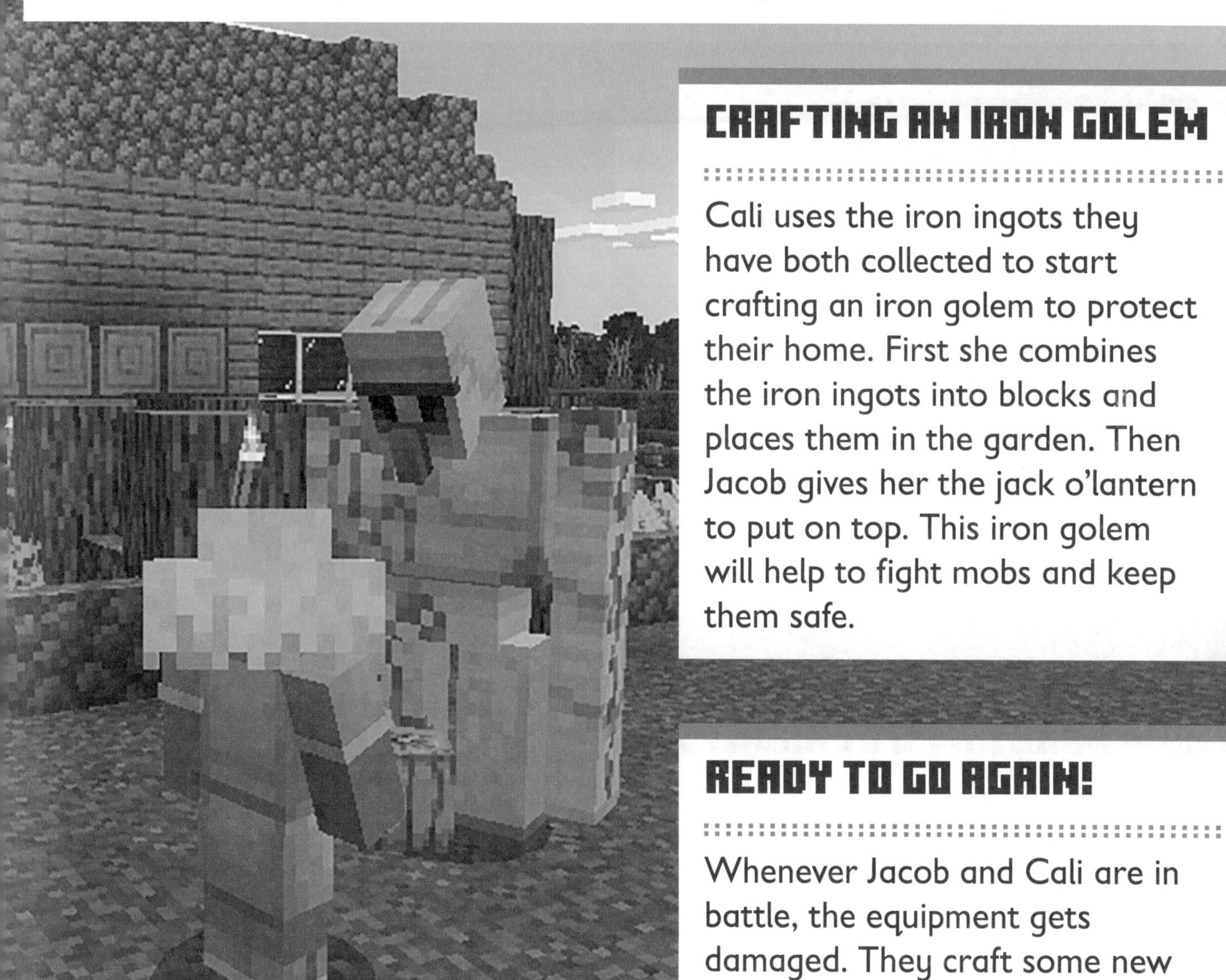

CRAFTING AN IRON GOLEM

Cali uses the iron ingots they have both collected to start crafting an iron golem to protect their home. First she combines the iron ingots into blocks and places them in the garden. Then Jacob gives her the jack o'lantern to put on top. This iron golem will help to fight mobs and keep them safe.

READY TO GO AGAIN!

Whenever Jacob and Cali are in battle, the equipment gets damaged. They craft some new swords and armour for both of them to use. As the day ends, both heroes are tired but looking forward to the next chapter of their adventures.

MEASUREMENT

GLORIOUS GREENERY

Finding a jungle is always spectacular because it blooms with lots of green colours. The jungle trees are much taller than any other type in the Overworld. The falling vines make the jungle feel dense and closed in because it's difficult to see far. Cocoa beans can grow on trees and bamboo can be found. The only other food that grows in the jungle is melons.

JUNGLE RESOURCES

Almost everything can be collected, broken down and transported – trees become logs, and logs become planks. You can regrow bamboo at home base. Cocoa beans and melons can be chopped and eaten or regrown. You can cut down the vines with shears or use them to climb the tall trees.

HOW ABOUT A PET PARROT?

Giant pandas, ocelots and parrots live in the jungle. Each of these animals can be fed a particular food – giant pandas like bamboo, ocelots eat fish and parrots enjoy seeds.

A jungle is bursting with resources and any adventurer will leave with full inventories of food and wood (and possibly even a tame parrot!).

JOURNEYING TO THE JUNGLE

Cali leaves base to explore. From a nearby mountain, she spots what looks like a jungle: tall trees and possibly bamboo stalks. With her tools ready and an empty inventory, she sets out to gather some wood, find animals, and possibly harvest some yummy cocoa beans to make cookies.

LENGTH AND HEIGHT

Cali arrives at the jungle. The trees are huge! She spends some time just looking at them and wondering how tall they are.

1

Which of the trees is taller?

Tick (✓) the box for the taller tree.

2

Look at each vine labelled A and B. The scale in the middle shows how tall each vine measures in blocks. Write how tall each vine measures.

A

B

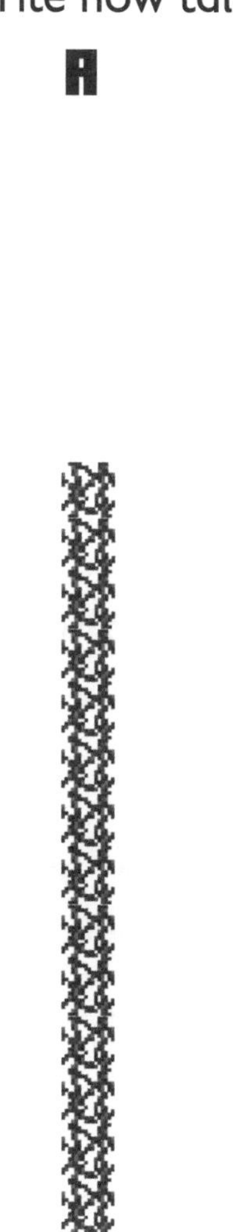

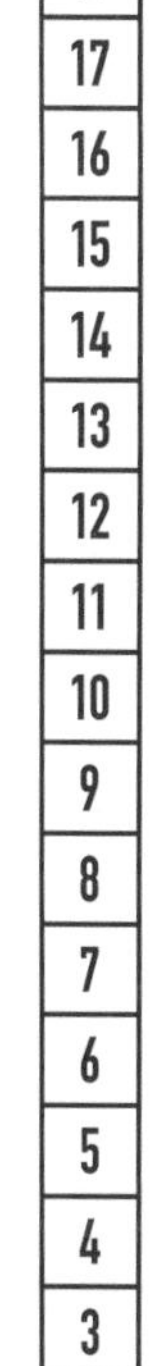

blocks tall

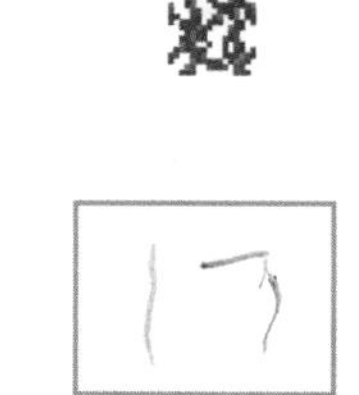

blocks tall

COLOUR IN HOW MANY EMERALDS YOU EARNED

WEIGHT AND CAPACITY

The jungle is amazing. Cali thinks back to the acacia and birch trees she has seen so far and compares them to a jungle tree. She pictures the three trees next to each other.

 1

Write the word **heavier** or the word **lighter** in each space below.

a) The jungle tree is .... than the acacia tree.

b) The birch tree is .... than the acacia tree.

As Cali moves between the trees, she finds a pond of water. She uses some buckets to take water on her journey… just in case.

 2

a) Look at the two choices below. Which number of buckets would you choose to fill a hole quicker? Tick (✓) the box for your choice.

 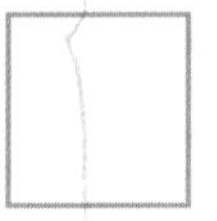

b) Look again at the two sets of buckets in part a).

Now complete the sentence.

Three .... of water would fill a hole faster because they

have a greater .... than ....

Cali spots a panda among the bamboo stalks. Pandas love to roll around and chomp on bamboo. Cali wonders how much the panda weighs.

3

These scales show how much a panda and an ocelot might weigh.

Look at the scales and complete the sentences below each of them.

a)

The panda weighs  blocks.

b)

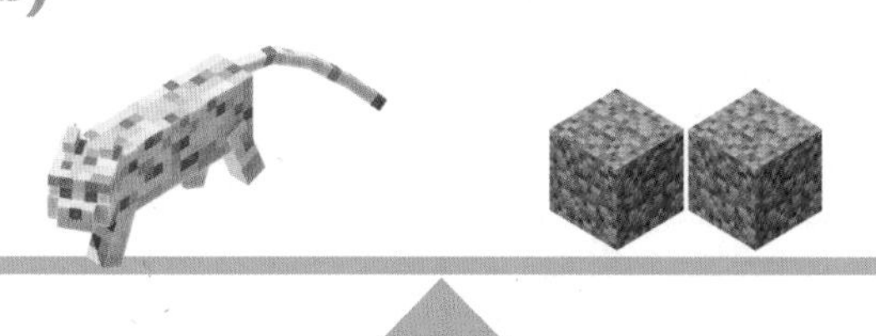

The ocelot weighs  blocks.

As Cali walks further, she finds a small village. There are only a few houses and a small farm. She finds a composter near the beetroot crops and looks at how it fills up when flowers, seeds or waste are put in.

4

These diagrams show how full four composters (numbered 1 to 4) are. Draw a line to join each description to the correct diagram.

a)

full

empty

half full

one quarter full

1

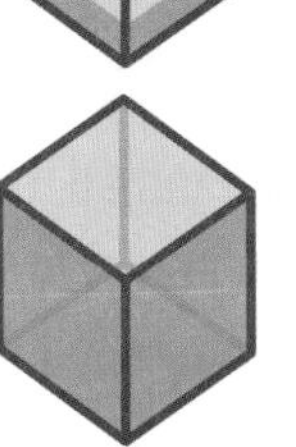

2

3

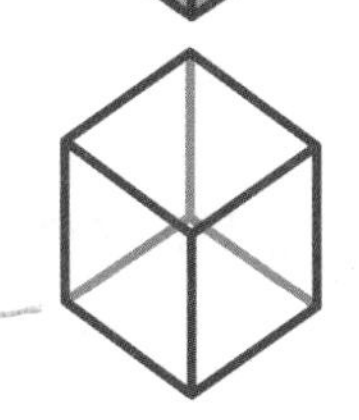

4

b) Complete the sentences with either the word **more** or the word **less**.

Composter 1 has .... than composter 4. Composter 3 has .... than composter 2.

COLOUR IN HOW MANY EMERALDS YOU EARNED

TIME

Cali sees some beautiful parrots flying around. She would like to tame one to keep it as a pet. It would sit on her shoulder and keep her company. Parrots love to eat seeds.

Draw a line to match each of the four words to the pictures to show the order Cali needs to do things to tame a parrot.

First

Second

Next

Last

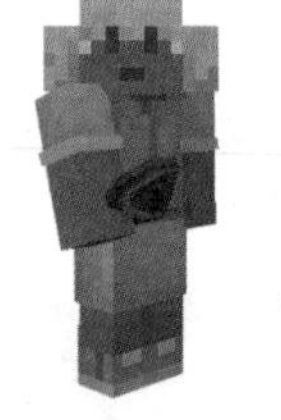

Cali and her new parrot friend are ready to keep exploring. She is thinking about her day so far and what else it may bring.

Write the correct word in each space to show the order of events in Cali's day.

tomorrow	morning	afternoon	evening

Cali woke up in the ...., ready for the day ahead.

During the ...., Cali explored the jungle and harvested items. Cali will go to bed in the .... When she wakes up ...., it will be morning again.

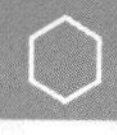

In the jungle, the trees grow so close together that it can be difficult to tell what time it is. Cali is glad she crafted a map and compass to find her way in the dark.

3

Read the times of the clocks. Circle the correct time for each clock.

12 o'clock 2 o'clock

7 o'clock 1 o'clock

Half-past 2 Half-past 5

Half-past 9 Half-past 3

4

Draw hands on the clocks so Cali knows what time it is.

3 o'clock

Half-past 10

COLOUR IN HOW MANY EMERALDS YOU EARNED

MONEY

Cali has harvested lots of wood in the jungle. She has also found melon and cocoa beans to take home. As she walks home, she spots a wandering trader. While Cali spends some emeralds with the trader, answer these questions about coins and notes you should know.

Look at all these coins.

How many of each type of coin can you see?

1p    10p    £1 

2

Write down the value of these coins and notes.

a) 

....

b) 

....

c) 

....

d) 

....

e) 

....

f) 

....

g) 

....

COLOUR IN HOW MANY EMERALDS YOU EARNED

ADVENTURE ROUND-UP

A NICE DAY OUT

Cali had a lovely day in the jungle. She took some time away from fighting to find new items and relax. She loved seeing new trees and plants. Plus, she made a new friend in her pet parrot.

FAVOURITE FRUIT

Jacob and Cali have already built a house, explored new places, crafted lots of new items and even gained some friends.

COOKIES AND MILK FOR SUPPER

Before Cali goes to bed, she uses some of the jungle wood to build a small room to keep her parrot. Meanwhile, Jacob makes some cookies as a treat for all the adventuring so far. Perfect with milk from their very own cows!

GEOMETRY

A COSY PLACE TO LIVE

The house started as somewhere to stay safe at night. It has become a nice little home, with lots of cosy comforts.

HOME IMPROVEMENTS

As the sun rises on another day, Jacob and Cali decide to do some jobs in and around the house.

2-D SHAPES

Jacob is constructing a new building near to the house. It will be used as a storage room, filled with chests. He chooses the wood he wants and starts laying blocks in different shapes.

Look at the designs. Draw lines to join the word labels to the shapes you can see on the designs.

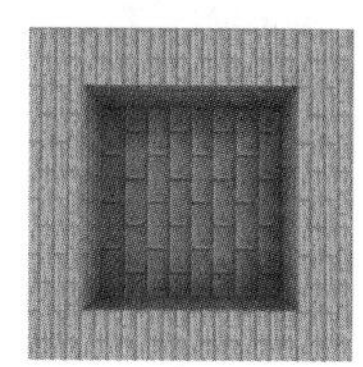

Square	**Rectangle**

Jacob decides to construct a pond between the new building and the house. He will place sand around the pond to grow sugar cane.

2

Here are two possible shapes of pond:

A

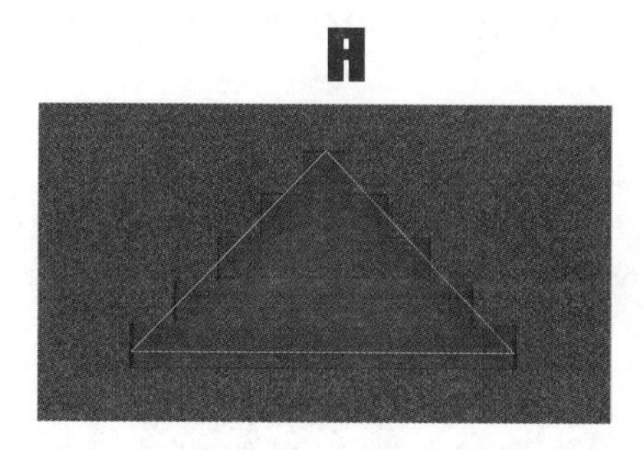

B

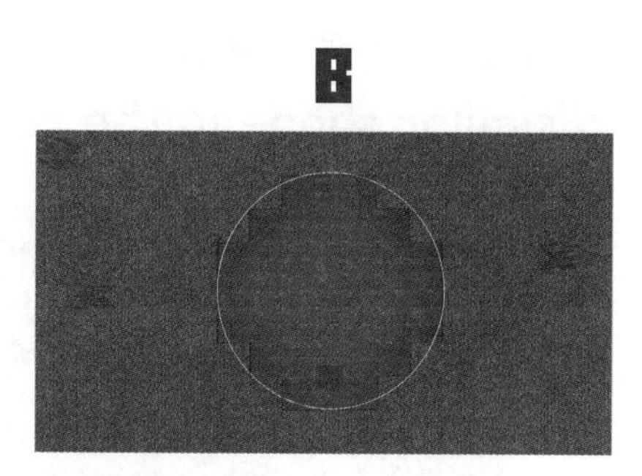

Tick (✓) the correct box to answer each question.

a) What shape is pond A? Circle ☐ Triangle ☐

b) What shape is pond B? Circle ☐ Triangle ☐

Jacob steps back to look at his new storage building.

3

Jacob draws this picture of the front of his storage building.

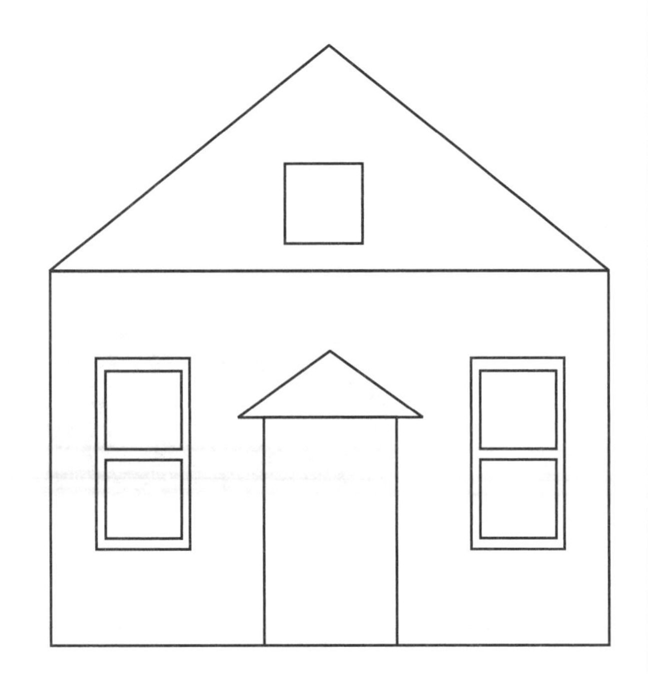

a) How many squares can you see?

b) How many rectangles can you see?

c) How many triangles can you see?

Jacob returns to the house. He stands at the door and looks around the main room.

4

Look at the picture of the room. Draw a line from each shape on the left to match it with a similar shape in the room.

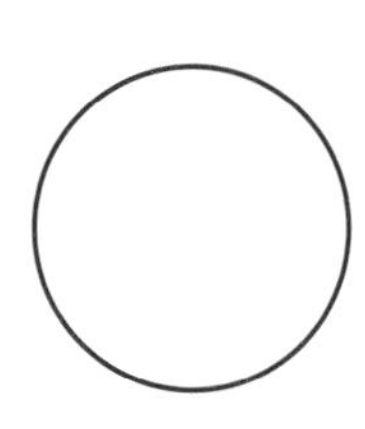

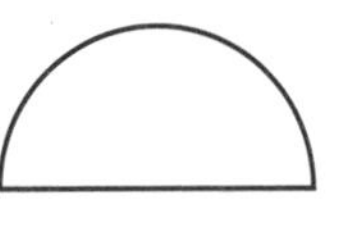

Jacob is using lots of materials to build extra furniture for the house. He wants the house to look really fun and be decorated with objects of different shapes. Help him to understand how many sides and corners the shapes below have.

5 

Fill in the boxes to show how many sides and corners these shapes have.

a) 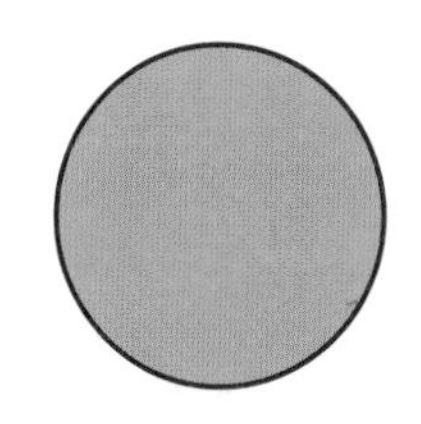

Number of sides

Number of corners

b) 

Number of sides 

Number of corners 

c) 

Number of sides

Number of corners 

d) 

Number of sides 

Number of corners 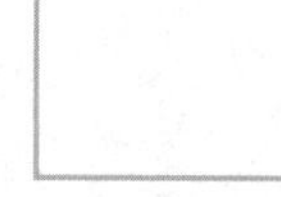

e) 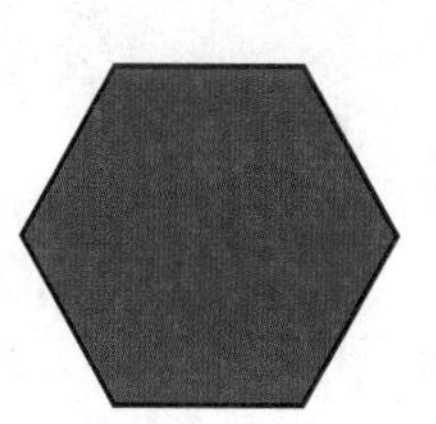

Number of sides

Number of corners

f) 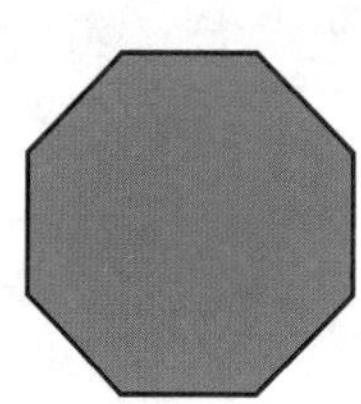

Number of sides 

Number of corners

COLOUR IN HOW MANY EMERALDS YOU EARNED

3-D SHAPES

Jacob has finished his jobs for the day. He starts thinking about fun things he could build. He enjoys creating new things.

1

Write down the name of each 3-D shape.

a) 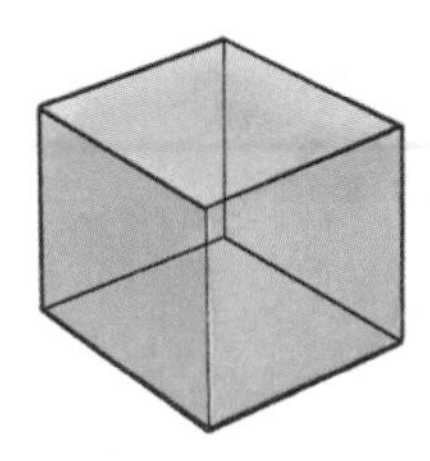

b) 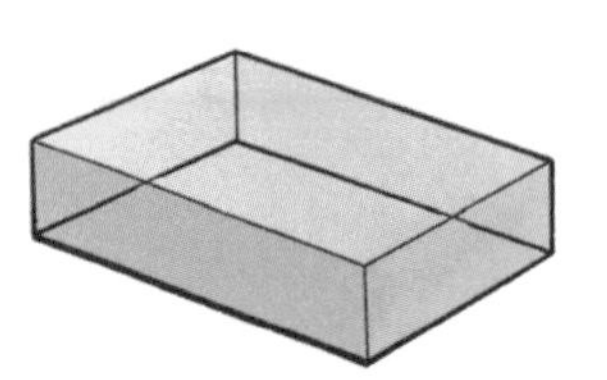

c) 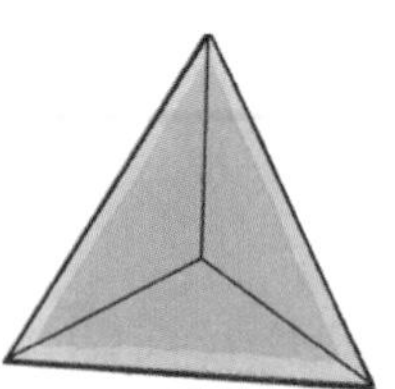

....

....

....

There are some shapes that Cali and Jacob can only imagine. What would they think of these?

 2 

Draw lines to join the name of each shape to the correct picture.

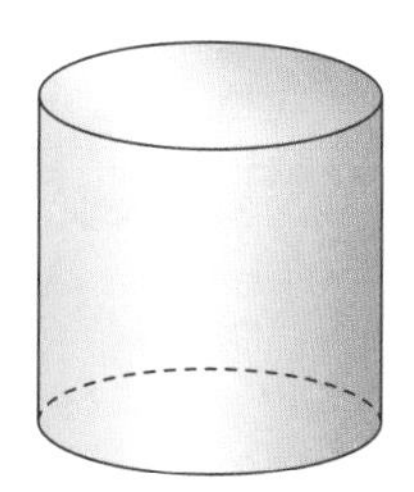

Cone

Cylinder

Square-based pyramid

Triangular prism

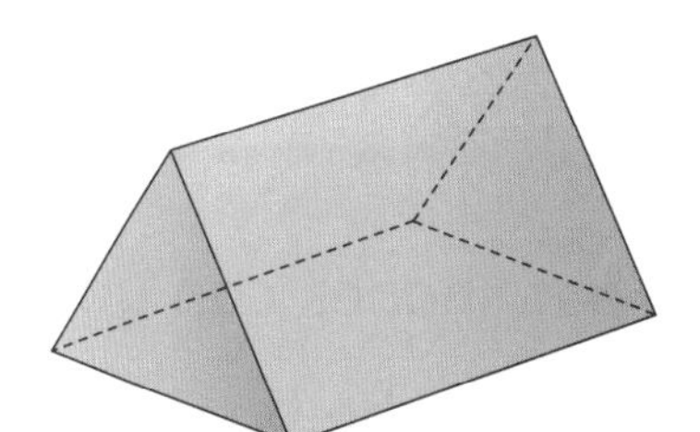

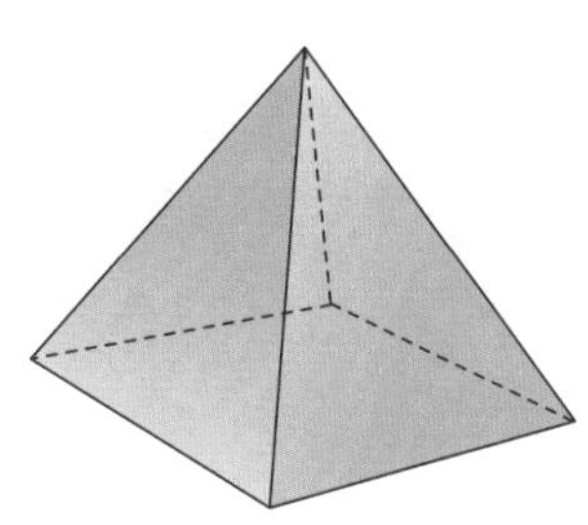

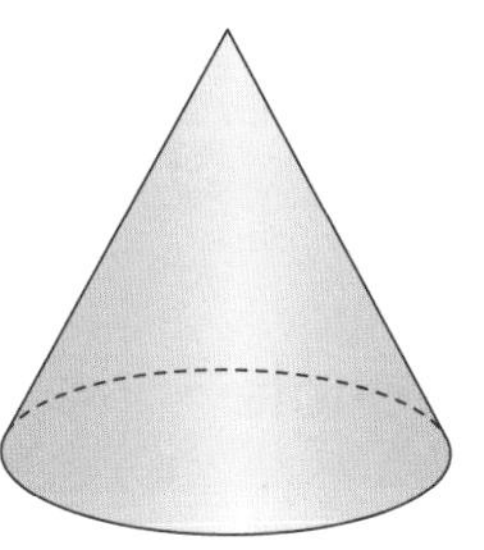

Jacob and Cali play a game which involves finding 3-D shapes around the house. The winner gets an emerald as a prize.

 3 

 Look at these objects. What 3-D shapes do they each most look like?

a) 

....

b) 

....

c) 

....

d) 

....

COLOUR IN HOW MANY EMERALDS YOU EARNED

DIFFERENT SHAPES

Jacob is thinking about the equipment they'll need later. They can't fight tough enemies with just iron swords. He's daydreaming about a diamond sword.

1

What shapes can you see in this diagram of a sword?

Tick (✓) the boxes for all the shapes that you can see.

Square ☐

Circle ☐

Rectangle ☐

Triangle ☐

Hexagon ☐

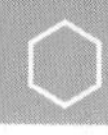

Jacob mentions to Cali that his next target is to find some diamonds. She surprises him with one she found in the jungle village. Jacob can't take his eyes off the gem. It's beautiful.

2

Here is another diamond shape.

Count the sides and corners.

Sides

Corners

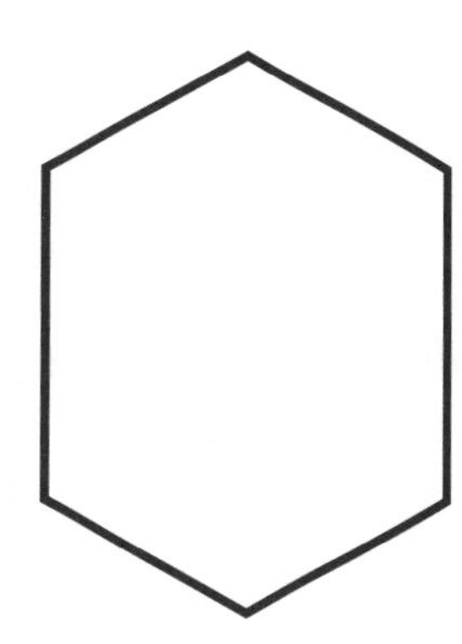

Jacob promises to keep the diamond safe until they have more. Then they will craft better weapons and armour! As Jacob puts the diamond away, he looks through the other materials in the chest.

3

Draw lines to join each object to the shape that it most looks like.

Cuboid

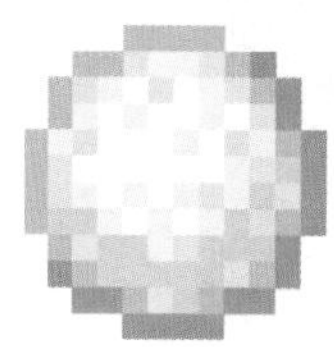

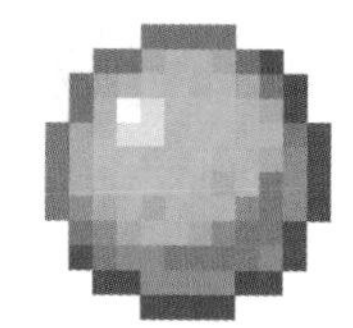

Sphere

COLOUR IN HOW MANY EMERALDS YOU EARNED

DESCRIBING POSITION

Jacob and Cali are proud of how much they've done so far. Just look at the main room of their house. They've crafted so many wonderful things to make it look nice and cosy. They have used pink granite for the centre of the floor and have placed a carpet across it.

Use this picture to answer questions 1–4.

Add some more items in the correct place in the picture above.

a) Draw a plant on top of the crafting table.

b) Draw a chest in front of the blue bed.

c) Draw a framed picture on the wall.

 2 

Look at the picture again on page 52. Choose the correct word from the box to complete each sentence.

chest	door	carpet

a) The .... is on top of the bookshelves.

b) The .... is in the middle of the granite.

3 

Look at the picture again on page 52. Now answer these questions.

a) What can you see above the blue bed, between the window and the clock?

....

b) What colours are the two squares in the middle of the carpet?

....

c) Look through the window on the right. What can you see outside?

....

4 

Write a sentence to describe where the red bed is.

....

....

COLOUR IN HOW MANY EMERALDS YOU EARNED

DESCRIBING MOVEMENT

To help decide where they might put new furniture, Jacob and Cali imagine looking into another room from above.

Use this picture to answer questions 1–3.

Cali is looking around the room.

a) Which object is Cali facing? ....

b) Which object is behind Cali? ....

c) Fill in the missing word to complete the sentence.

The crafting table is in the .... of the room.

2

Fill in the missing word to complete each sentence.

a) Cali faces the bed.

She makes a full turn.

She is now facing the ....

b) Cali faces the bed.

She makes a half turn.

She is now facing the ....

c) Cali faces the bed.

She makes a quarter turn clockwise

She is now facing the ....

d) Cali faces the bed.

She makes a three-quarter turn anti-clockwise.

She is now facing the ....

3

Cali faces the crafting table.

She makes a half turn. Then she makes a quarter turn to the right.

Which item is she facing after these movements? ....

COLOUR IN HOW MANY EMERALDS YOU EARNED

LEFT, RIGHT, FORWARDS AND BACKWARDS

Here is a grid that shows a plan of a room in Jacob's house. It shows where he is standing and where different objects are in the room.

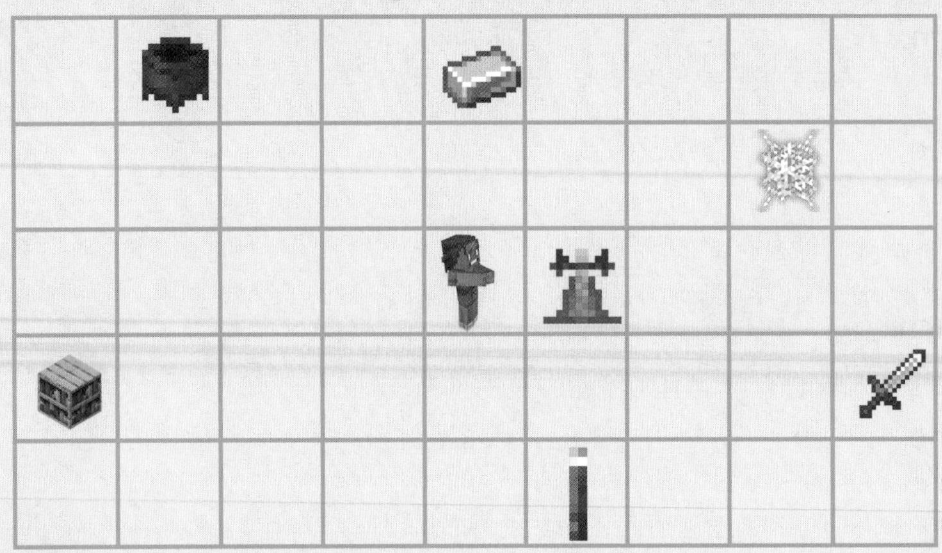

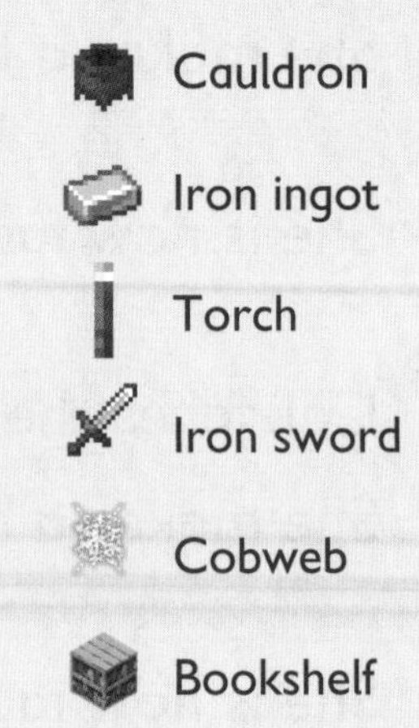

1

Jacob is facing the brewing stand. He moves four squares backwards.

Which object is he now next to? ....

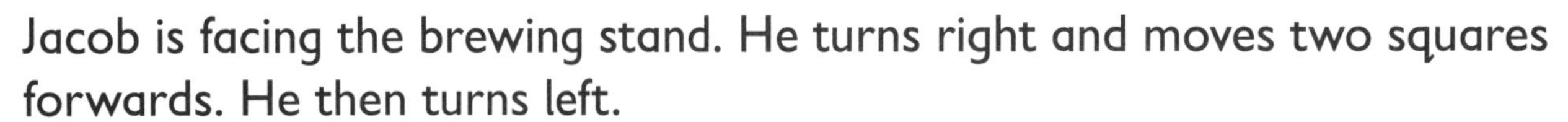

2

Jacob is facing the brewing stand. He turns right and moves two squares forwards. He then turns left.

Which object is he facing now? ....

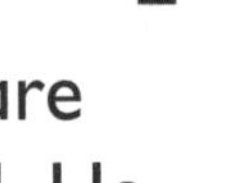

3

Jacob is facing the brewing stand. He turns left and moves one square forward. He then turns left again and moves three squares forward. He then turns right.

Which object is he facing now? ....

COLOUR IN HOW MANY EMERALDS YOU EARNED

ADVENTURE ROUND-UP

HAPPY HOME

Jacob and Cali share a cake and talk about all the exciting things that they have done and seen. It's already been quite an adventure! They feel safe and happy in their new home.

WHAT'S THAT NOISE?

From outside, there's a strange noise. Something is spooking the animals. Jacob and Cali dash towards the door and throw it open. In the dark of night, they can only see shadows. The heroes pull out their swords.

PILLAGER ALERT!

As the shadows come into the light around the fences, it's not zombies. It's not skeletons either. It's worse. It's a group of pillagers! They're armed with crossbows and they're hopping up and down in anger.

A HAPPY ENDING?

Jacob and Cali prepare to defend their home. We'll leave it to your imagination to decide how the battle ends!

ANSWERS

Page 5

1 4 [1 emerald]

2

12 tulips | 16 poppies | 20 dandelions

[1 emerald each]

Pages 6–7

1 11 24 36 45 50 [1 emerald each]

2 a) 26 [1 emerald]

b) 31 [1 emerald]

c) 33 [1 emerald]

3 a) 42 [1 emerald]

b) 39 [1 emerald]

c) 35 [1 emerald]

Pages 8–9

1 6 [1 emerald]

2 15 [1 emerald]

3 20 [1 emerald]

4

12 | 25 | 3

[1 emerald each]

5 Three emeralds circled [1 emerald]

Pages 10–11

1 a) (8 + 1 =) 9 [1 emerald]

b) (14 + 1 =) 15 [1 emerald]

c) (17 + 1 =) 18 [1 emerald]

d) (22 + 1 =) 23 [1 emerald]

e) (29 + 1 =) 30 [1 emerald]

2 a) (5 – 1 =) 4 [1 emerald]

b) (10 – 1 =) 9 [1 emerald]

c) (16 – 1 =) 15 [1 emerald]

d) (27 – 1 =) 26 [1 emerald]

e) (30 – 1 =) 29 [1 emerald]

3 4 [1 emerald]

Pages 12–13

1 less [1 emerald]

2 more [1 emerald]

3

[1 emerald]

4 a) equals [1 emerald]

b) less than [1 emerald]

c) more than [1 emerald]

Page 14

1

10 | 19 | 13

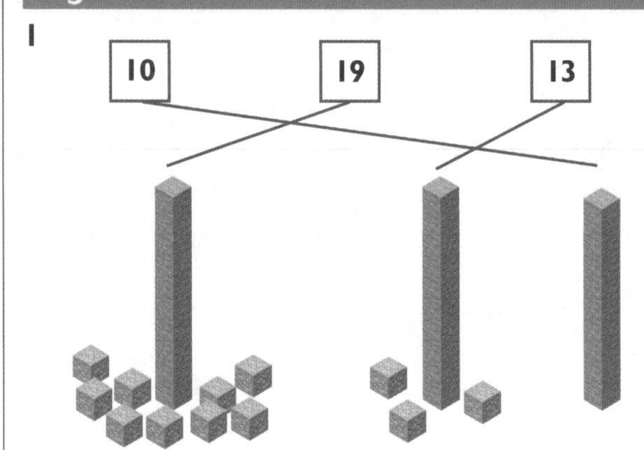

[1 emerald each]

2 14 [1 emerald]

12 [1 emerald]

Page 17

1 Four red mushrooms drawn [1 emerald]

2 a) 8 [1 emerald]

b) 8 [1 emerald]

3 Six logs crossed out [1 emerald]

4 a) 6 [1 emerald]

b) 6 [1 emerald]

Pages 18–19

1 Five rabbits drawn; total is 9 [1 emerald]

2 20 [1 emerald]

3 10 [1 emerald]

4 2 [1 emerald]

Pages 20–21

1 Eight ingots crossed out; 10 [1 emerald each]

2 Four skeletons drawn; 12 [1 emerald each]

3 16 [1 emerald]

4 Boxes joined as follows:
Cali uses up 5 lumps of coal. How many coal does she have left? 15 lumps [1 emerald]
Cali uses up 12 lumps of coal. How many coal does she have left? 8 lumps [1 emerald]
Cali uses up 15 lumps of coal. How many coal does she have left? 5 lumps [1 emerald]

Page 22

1 **a)** 2 [1 emerald]
b) 4 [1 emerald]
2 **a)** 9 [1 emerald]

Page 25

1 8 [1 emerald]
2 6 [1 emerald]
3 10 [1 emerald]

Pages 26–27

1 Five circles drawn around the pairs of cobwebs [1 emerald]
2 The right-hand picture should be ticked [1 emerald]
3 Three cobwebs should be drawn in each chamber [1 emerald]
4 4 [1 emerald]

Pages 28–29

1 6 [1 emerald]
2 30 [1 emerald]
3 40 [1 emerald]
4 **a)** 2 [1 emerald]
b) 4 [1 emerald]
c) 5 [1 emerald]
5 **a)** 10 [1 emerald]
b) 50 [1 emerald]
c) 20 [1 emerald]

Pages 30–31

1 4 [1 emerald]
2 4 porkchops [1 emerald]
3 4 hits × 5 damage = 20 damage [1 emerald]
4 9 skeletons [1 emerald]

Pages 32–33

1 One quarter [1 emerald]
2 $\frac{1}{2}$ [1 emerald]
3 One quarter [1 emerald]
4 **a)** One quarter [1 emerald]
b) Halfway [1 emerald]
c) Three quarters [1 emerald]

Page 35

1 Any 4 pumpkins circled [1 emerald]
4 [1 emerald]
2 Any 2 pumpkins circled [1 emerald]
2 [1 emerald]

Page 37

1 The second tree should be ticked [1 emerald]
2 A: 14 [1 emerald]
B: 18 [1 emerald]

Pages 38–39

1 **a)** heavier [1 emerald]
b) lighter [1 emerald]
2 **a)** Three buckets ticked [1 emerald]
b) buckets; capacity; one bucket [1 emerald each]
3 **a)** 6 [1 emerald]
b) 2 [1 emerald]
4 **a)** Lines drawn as follows:
'full' joined to composter 2 [1 emerald]
'empty' joined to composter 4 [1 emerald]
'half full' joined to composter 3 [1 emerald]
'one quarter full' joined to composter 1 [1 emerald]
b) more; less [1 emerald each]

Pages 40–41

1
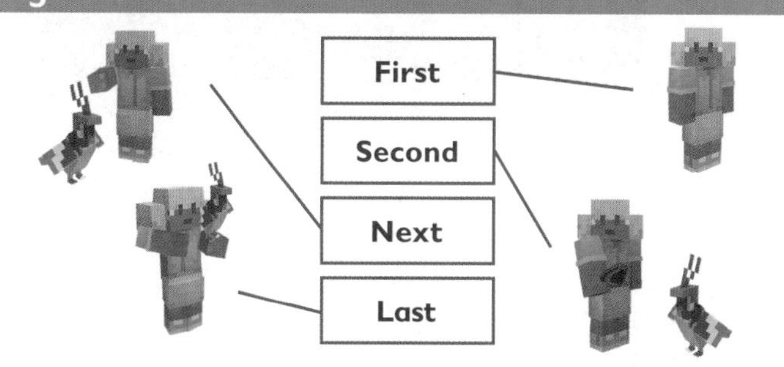

[1 emerald each]

2 morning; afternoon; evening; tomorrow [1 emerald each]

3 Times circled as follows from top left, left to right:
2 o'clock [1 emerald]
7 o'clock [1 emerald]
Half-past 5 [1 emerald]
Half-past 9 [1 emerald]

4

[1 emerald]

[1 emerald]

Page 42

1 1p: 5 10p: 4 £1: 3 [1 emerald each]

2 a) 2p [1 emerald]
b) 50p [1 emerald]
c) 5p [1 emerald]
d) 20p [1 emerald]
e) £2 [1 emerald]
f) £5 [1 emerald]
g) £20 [1 emerald]

Pages 45–47

1

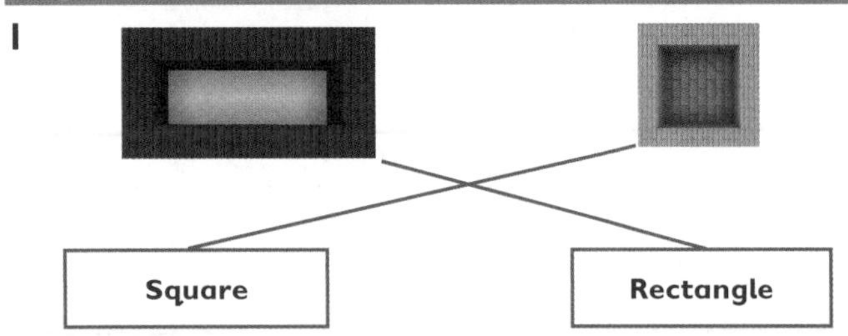

[1 emerald each]

2 a) Triangle [1 emerald]
b) Circle [1 emerald]

3 a) 5 [1 emerald]
b) 4 [1 emerald]
c) 2 [1 emerald]

4

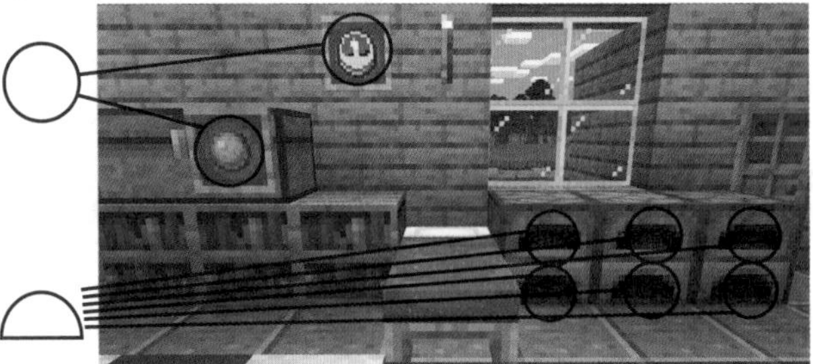

[1 emerald for circles identified;
1 emerald for semi-circles identified]

5 a) Sides: 1 Corners: 0 [1 emerald]
b) Sides: 3 Corners: 3 [1 emerald]
c) Sides: 4 Corners: 4 [1 emerald]
d) Sides: 4 Corners: 4 [1 emerald]
e) Sides: 6 Corners: 6 [1 emerald]
f) Sides: 8 Corners: 8 [1 emerald]

Pages 48–49

1 a) Cube [1 emerald]
b) Cuboid [1 emerald]
c) Pyramid (or Tetrahedron) [1 emerald]

2

Cone
Cylinder
Square-based pyramid
Triangular prism

[1 emerald each]

3 a) Cuboid [1 emerald]
b) Pyramid [1 emerald]
c) Cube [1 emerald]
d) Sphere [1 emerald]

Pages 50–51

1 These should be ticked:
Square; Rectangle; Triangle [1 emerald each]

2 Sides: 6 [1 emerald]
Corners: 6 [1 emerald]

3

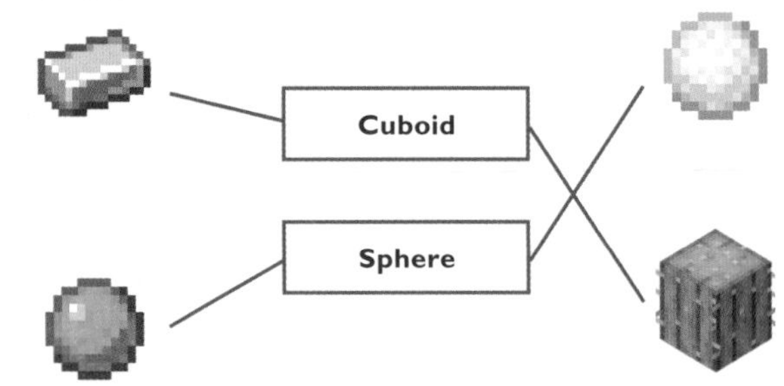

[1 emerald each]

Pages 52–53

1 a) A plant should be drawn on the crafting table (which is located below the left-hand window) [1 emerald]
b) A chest should be drawn in front of the blue bed [1 emerald]
c) A framed picture should be drawn anywhere on the wall [1 emerald]

2 a) chest [1 emerald]
b) carpet [1 emerald]

3 a) a torch [1 emerald]
b) black and white [1 emerald]
c) Any suitable answer.
Examples: a fence; a garden; grass [1 emerald]

4 Any suitable answer.
Example:
The red bed is between the crafting table and the bookshelves. [1 emerald]

Pages 54–55

1 a) bed [1 emerald]
b) door [1 emerald]
c) middle (or centre) [1 emerald]

2 **a)** bed [1 emerald]
 b) door [1 emerald]
 c) crafting table [1 emerald]
 d) crafting table [1 emerald]

3 bed [1 emerald]

Page 56

1 bookshelf [1 emerald]

2 torch [1 emerald]

3 cauldron [1 emerald]

TRADE IN YOUR EMERALDS!

Well done for helping Jacob and Cali to complete their adventures! Along the way, you earned emeralds for your hard work answering the questions. This merchant is waiting for you to spend your gems. Pretend you're preparing for a night-time adventure and you know you'll fight lots of mobs. Which items would you buy to make sure you can survive the night?

Ask a grown-up to help you count all your emeralds and write the total in this box.

HMMM?

SHOP INVENTORY

- DIAMOND CHESTPLATE: 30 EMERALDS
- DIAMOND HELMET: 20 EMERALDS
- DIAMOND LEGGINGS: 25 EMERALDS
- DIAMOND SWORD: 25 EMERALDS
- DIAMOND PICKAXE: 20 EMERALDS
- CROSSBOW: 15 EMERALDS
- ARROWS OF DECAY: 10 EMERALDS
- FIREWORKS: 5 EMERALDS
- GOLDEN APPLE: 10 EMERALDS
- COOKED SALMON: 10 EMERALDS
- BEETROOT SOUP: 10 EMERALDS
- ENCHANTED BOOK: 15 EMERALDS
- POTION OF REGENERATION: 30 EMERALDS
- POTION OF INVISIBILITY: 35 EMERALDS
- POTION OF STRENGTH: 35 EMERALDS

That's a lot of emeralds. Well done! Remember, just like real money, you don't need to spend it all. Sometimes it's good to save up.